Advanced Higher

English

2003 Exam

2004 Exam

2005 Exam

2006 Exam

© Scottish Qualifications Authority

All rights reserved. Copying prohibited. No part of this publication may be reproduced, stored in a retrieval system, or transmitted in any form or by any means, electronic, mechanical, photocopying, recording or otherwise.

First exam published in 2003.
Published by Leckie & Leckie Ltd, 3rd Floor, 4 Queen Street, Edinburgh EH2 1JE
tel: 0131 220 6831 fax: 0131 225 9987 enquiries@leckieandleckie.co.uk www.leckieandleckie.co.uk

ISBN 1-84372-453-7 ISBN-13 978-1-84372-453-7

A CIP Catalogue record for this book is available from the British Library.

Printed in Scotland by Scotprint.

Leckie & Leckie is a division of Granada Learning Limited.

Leckie & Leckie is grateful to the copyright holders, as credited at the back of the book, for permission to use their material. Every effort has been made to trace the copyright holders and to obtain their permission for the use of copyright material. Leckie & Leckie will gladly receive information enabling them to rectify any error or omission in subsequent editions.

2003 | Advanced Higher

[BLANK PAGE]

X200/701

NATIONAL QUALIFICATIONS 2003

FRIDAY, 16 MAY
1.00 PM – 4.00 PM

ENGLISH
ADVANCED HIGHER

There are six sections in this paper.

If you have submitted a Creative Writing folio **or** an Oral Communication videotape, you must answer only **one** question.

Otherwise, you must answer **two** questions.

The maximum time allowed for any question is **1 hour 30 minutes**.

If you answer only **one question**

- you must leave the examination room **after 1 hour 30 minutes**.

If you answer **two questions**

- each question must be taken **from a different section**
- each answer must be written in **a separate answer booklet**.

You must identify each question you attempt by indicating clearly

- **the title of the section** from which the question has been taken
- **the number of the question** within that section.

You must also write inside the front cover of each of your answer booklets

- **the topic** of your Specialist Study
- **the texts** used in your Specialist Study.

LIB X200/701 6/3120

©

Section 1—Language

You must answer **one question only** in this section.

NB If you attempt **Topic A**, you must indicate clearly the particular geographical area nominated by your school or college and approved by SQA.

Topic A—The use of English in a particular geographical area

1. Describe the features of a particular regional variety of English and include a discussion of its historical development and its relationship to other regional varieties or standard English.

2. How important is language to a sense of regional identity?

Discuss this issue in relation to a regional variety of English you have researched. In your answer you might consider:

- distinctive features of the language
- its use in everyday communication and/or literature
- attitudes to this particular variety.

Topic B—Variations in the use of English related to social class

3. "*If we are to arrive at an accurate picture of the relationship between language and social class, we must be able to measure both linguistic and social phenomena so that we can relate the two.*"

From your reading and research in language studies, describe:

- methods of investigating language and social class
- the linguistic features associated with different social classes.

4. In what ways do you regard the linguistic characteristics of the following text to be typical of a working-class conversational style?

The transcription is quite light, and indicates only:

... pause
( ) non-verbal information
[ ] indistinct or missing features.

Nan: An one night A went to the bingo an A won, never won anything in ma life, right? Old Auntie Susie was there, mind? Archie's Auntie Susie? And A won twenty-four poun an A wis wi ma Auntie Margaret and eh she shouted "Bingo! Bingo!" and A was goin "What is it?" She went "Ye've won, ye've won!" an A didnae even know. A went "Oh have A won? Right." An A jumped off the seat **...** the seat fell. It was thon widden seats **(***Laughs***)** **[**An A went tae**]** sat back doon **...** and I sat **...** I was that excited sat on the flair. So then A gets my twenty-four poun and we rins away hame **...** and A **...** there wis Auntie Susie, there wis the weans, there wis oor Betty, A don't know how many wis in, an A wis giein them aw two poun each. An A **...** an A gied Auntie Susie two poun, an everybody two poun and A got **...** an A got to the end an A went like that **(***Looks at empty hand***)**.

Di: You'd no[t]hing left?

Nan: A'd a poun! [Only had] a poun! Ah, naw, A had ... A'd gied Auntie Susie a poun because by the time that she was at the end, A'd gied everybody two poun an aw that an A got ... By the time A got to her, A went "If A gie her two poun A'm no getting anything," an A gied her a poun. A got a poun oot ma twenty-four poun!

Jackie: Twenty-four poun was a lot o money then.

Nan: Oh [it wis].

Topic C—Variations in the use of English related to gender

5. "*Many misunderstandings in conversation between males and females occur because men and women make different assumptions about what conversation is for, and so they use conversation in different ways.*"

   To what extent do you agree with the above statement?

   In your answer, you might wish to comment on:

   - the expectations that males and females bring to conversation
   - the styles of conversation adopted by males and females
   - typical examples of male-female conversational misunderstandings and how these might be explained.

6. Compare and contrast the topics and styles of conversation associated with male and female single-sex groups.

Topic D—The linguistic characteristics of informal conversation

For both questions on this topic, consider the following text. It is an extract from a transcription of an informal conversational exchange between Deborah, the hostess at a dinner party, and Peter, one of her guests. Two other guests, Steve and Sally, listen.

It contains the following transcription codes:

..	noticeable pause or break in rhythm (less than a half second)
...	half second pause, as measured by stop watch; an extra dot is added for each half second, hence:
....	full second pause
′	marks primary stress
`	marks secondary stress
ˈ	marks high pitch on a word
⌐	marks high pitch on a phrase, continuing until punctuation
⌊	marks low pitch on phrase, continuing until punctuation
.	marks sentence-final falling intonation
?	marks yes/no question rising intonation
–	marks a glottal stop, or abrupt cutting off of a sound
:	indicates a lengthened vowel sound
,	marks phrase-final intonation

musical notation is used for amplitude and appears under the line:

p piano (spoken softly)

dec spoken slowly

f forte (spoken loudly)

/?/ indicates transcription impossible

[indicates overlapping speech (two people talking at the same time)

˥ indicates that the second utterance is latched onto the first, without a perceptible pause.

Written punctuation, such as full stops and commas, has been avoided.

(1) Deborah: Do you réad? ....

(2) Peter: Do I réad? ...

(3) Deborah: Do you rèad things just for fún?

...

(4) Peter: Yeah .... Right now I'm reading Norma Jean the Termite Queen [*laughs*]

(5) Deborah: ⌐Whàt's thát? ... Norma Jean uh: Marilyn Monroe?
f

(6) Peter: It's .. ˌNo: . It's a book about ...... a housewife /??/
dec

(7) Deborah: Is it a ⌐nóvel or whàt?

(8) Peter: ˈÌt's a ˌnovel.

(9) Deborah: ˈYeah?

(10) Peter: Before that .... I read the French Lieutenant's Woman.
⌐Have you [read that?

(11) Deborah: [Oh yeah? No. Whó wrote that?

(12) Peter: John Fowles.

(13) Deborah: Yeah I've heárd that he's good.

(14) Peter: ˈHe's a ⌞gréat writer. ˈÍ think he's one of the ⌞bést

Deborah: hm

(15) Deborah: /?/

(16) Peter: ˈHe's really ˌgoòd.

(17) Deborah: /?/

(18) Peter: But Í get very bùsy. .... [Y'know?

(19) Deborah: [Yeah, I– .. hàrdly éver reàd.

(20) Peter: What I've been dóing is cutting down on my sléep.

(21) Deborah: Oy! [*sighs*]

(22) Peter: And I've been [Steve *laughs*] ..... and I s

(23) Deborah: Í do that tòo

but it's páinful.

(24) Peter: Yeah. Fi:ve, six hours a ˈníght,

and

(25) Deborah: Oh Gód, hòw can you dó it? You survíve?

(26) Peter: Yeah làte afternoon méetings are hàrd. .... But outside

Deborah: mmm

of thát I can keep gòing pretty well

(27) Deborah: Not sleeping enough is

térrible .... I'd múch rather not eàt than not sleèp.

þ

[Sally *laughs*]

7. The above transcript is thoroughly annotated to show various features of pronunciation. Describe the issues involved in transcribing speech, and explain why it might be useful to have the kind of information given here.

8. Discuss the ways in which the participants in the above transcript show *rapport*, for example, sympathy and support. You may also include other examples of demonstrations of *rapport* from your own study of informal conversation.

Topic E—The linguistic characteristics of political communication

9. From your own exploration of the use of language in political communication, explain how politicians seek to persuade their audience to support their point of view. You should consider how politicians use rhetorical devices and other linguistic strategies to:

- characterise their supporters and opponents
- appeal to the emotions
- address their audience(s).

10. The following text is an extract from the Official Report of the Scottish Parliament on First Minister's Question Time (10th January 2002). The First Minister, Mr Jack McConnell, is answering questions about the acceptance of the newly-launched Euro by Scottish tourist attractions.

Each contribution to the proceedings has been numbered.

Make a detailed analysis of the report, explaining how the context of the communicative event influences such characteristics as:

- the degree of formality
- the choice of vocabulary
- the use of questions to challenge and support the First Minister
- the strategies used by the First Minister in response to challenges
- the use of humour in the exchanges.

Tourist Attractions (Euro)

[1] **Mr Keith Raffan (Mid Scotland and Fife) (LD)**: To ask the First Minister what action the Scottish Executive is taking to ensure that all major tourist attractions accept the euro.

[2] **The First Minister (Mr Jack McConnell)**: The Executive supports the steps that have been taken by Scotland Europa, in conjunction with the UK Treasury, to provide advice and raise awareness of the need for all businesses, including those in the tourist industry, to be suitably prepared for the introduction of the euro. Of course, the decision whether to accept the euro is a commercial one for the businesses concerned. However, we have ensured, with the key organisations that cover the range of interests across the business community, that up-to-date advice and information are available to help businesses with their preparations.

[3] **Mr Raffan**: Is the First Minister aware that, of Edinburgh's top 10 paid tourist attractions, only one is so far accepting euro notes and coins? Does he agree that if the Tower of London, Hampton Court Palace and Chester zoo can accept the euro, so should Edinburgh Castle, Holyrood House and Edinburgh zoo? Will he join me in lobbying the Scottish Parliamentary Corporate Body to ensure that the Scottish Parliament does not continue to lag behind and that its shop, which attracts a considerable number of tourists, accepts the euro, rather than turning it away, as it has been doing in the past week?

[4] **The First Minister**: The prospect of a debate on whether the Parliament shop should accept the euro is enticing. It might lead to the Conservatives boycotting the Scottish Parliamentary Corporate Body in the same way as they boycott the Holyrood progress group. I hope that that would not be the case. I understand that the decisions that have been taken in Scotland's major tourist attractions—the majority of which are not planning to take euro cash this summer—were made following market research on whether accepting the euro would be a viable investment at this time. This morning, I asked Historic Scotland to keep that position under review. It will do that and we will receive regular reports on the progress that is being made.

[5] **Ms Margo MacDonald (Lothians) (SNP)**: Will the First Minister also ask Historic Scotland to keep under review the source of revenue from a much bigger market than euroland? Will our major tourist attractions please accept the US dollar also?

[6] **The First Minister**: I am unaware of any political party in the UK—although there may be one somewhere—that proposes that Scotland's currency should become the dollar, but I am aware of at least the medium-term potential for the euro to become the currency of Scotland and the UK. We are involved in a single market with the countries that have adopted the euro. The sensible point has been made that our shops, attractions and businesses should be able at least to trade in euros when appropriate. That makes much sense.

[7] **Mr David Davidson (North-East Scotland) (Con)**: I am sure that Scotland's businesses have taken heart from the First Minister's assurance that whether to accept any currency other than legal tender and what rate to charge for that are commercial decisions for businesses. I will take the First Minister further along the Historic Scotland route. He talked about the instructions that he has given the body. Does Historic Scotland receive guidance from the First Minister and his team, or is it a free-standing body that can make its own decisions, with a board that is accountable in the normal manner? In the past year, I have received several representations from people who work for the organisation. In how much detail does the First Minister instruct Historic Scotland, whether on the euro or other matters?

[8] **The First Minister**: I made it clear in my first answer that, in my conversation with Historic Scotland this morning, I asked it to keep the matter under review. It agreed to do so. That is the right relationship between the organisation and us.

[9] **Irene Oldfather (Cunninghame South) (Lab)**: Does the First Minister agree that the price transparency that will accompany the euro will be good for tourists and consumers throughout Europe? Does he join me in commending the Convention of Scottish Local Authorities for its work on promoting an information campaign in the public sector and in condemning the scaremongers, including Conservative members, who refuse to conduct the debate on the basis of the facts?

[10] **The First Minister**: I am always happy to condemn scaremongers—and sometimes Tories. The topic is serious. COSLA has acted responsibly in running that information campaign. It is vital that people know of the euro's potential impact on Scotland and the UK and of the need to prepare now to ensure that we have maximum trading opportunities with our main trading partners throughout the euro zone. That is an important part of the preparations that we should make to ensure that our economy survives the challenges of this and future years.

Topic F—The linguistic characteristics of tabloid journalism

11. Discuss and illustrate the ways in which tabloid newspapers describe individuals in terms of general categories such as gender, marital status, race, age.

12. "*Tabloid newspapers have to be lively because they offer themselves as a brand of entertainment.*"

Describe some of the principal linguistic means by which tabloid newspapers present serious issues in a "lively" way.

[Turn over

Section 2—Scottish Language

You must answer **one question only** in this section.

NB If you attempt **Topic A**, you must indicate clearly the particular geographical area nominated by your school or college and approved by SQA.

Topic A—The use of Scots in a particular geographical area

1. From your own research, describe in detail, the linguistic characteristics of the speech of any **one** geographical area in Scotland.

2. According to the Concise Scots Dictionary, the Scots language "*has never been wholly extinguished between the sixteenth century and the present day*".

   To what extent can you support this statement by drawing upon your knowledge of the language of **one** or **more than one** geographical area in Scotland?

Topic B—The linguistic characteristics of Scots as used in informal conversation

3. From your study of informal conversation in Scots, describe some of the ways in which different speakers use language to construct and negotiate meaning when they communicate.

4. Look carefully at the transcript which follows and think about, in particular, how the dynamic of the exchange works. Analyse how meaning is made and shared among the three speakers. You might focus on:

   - use of vocabulary
   - turn-taking
   - cooperative strategies used within the conversation.

   The transcription is quite light, and only indicates:

...	pause
( )	non-verbal information
[ ]	indistinct or missing features.

Dens Road Market

CA: You don't like Dundee?

A: Na, I hate Dundee.

CA: Dae ye?

A: I've went aff it. For some reason I've went aff it.

CA: You've got a lovely situation ... eh ... wi the river, ye know. I mean today when I was coming ...

A: Docks, [the] docks and aa that carry on.

B: But even the docks is worse noo. Know what I mean?

A: No . . . noth . . . nothing's changed.

B: It's aa the pollution that's in it. I mean aa the oil and aa the water an that. The Tey's no clean nae mair.

A: Nuh. Well it used to be, it used to be clean once a time but no now.

B: No now.

CA: Would you have been able to swim in the Tay at any point?

A&B: No. No. Ye're jokin!

CA: Even out at Broughty Ferry, would you . . .

A: Oh, the Broughty Ferry beach, the beach is aa right in Broughty Ferry, is it, ye know.

B: [Course if ye] . . . if you'd swallaed the water you'd soon ken aboot it. You know what I mean.

A: Crocodiles and creepy-craalies.

B: Jist aa the stuff [that they] throw in the water doon there. Ken whit I mean. They'd throw any[t]hin in it.

A: Throw bottles and everything in it. I mean they fling aa their papers and everything. You['d] never know whit can happen.

B: Ye jist dinna ken . . .

A: The beach is no the same either.

CA: The what? The beach?

B: The beach. Broughty Ferry is the [worst].

A: It's getting worse. They never dae nothing wi it.

B: Nuh. No a tidy beach, ken whit I mean.

A: It's a mess.

CA: It's a shame. It's a shame cos it's a great asset havin the . . .

B: Ay.

A: Especially in the summer. It's braa in the summer doon [th]ere. Ah.

B: [Aabody] goes to it, like, but I mean.

A: But they aa sit in their cars. They dinna go to the . . . they dinna go doon to the sand nor to no[t]hin.

B: Know what I mean [they] sit in their cars man.

A: They aa sit in the cars wi' the doors open, ken. So . . . i . . . in other words, they're tryin to say "I'm no goin doon to that beach. You never know what's in it."

B: That's right.

Topic C—Variations in the use of Scots among older and younger people

5. "*Much but by no means all of the earlier Scots vocabulary has disappeared or is disappearing, but the grammar shows historical stability and continuity.*"

With reference to your study of the use of Scots among older and younger people, and illustrating your answer with examples, how far would you agree?

6. "*Young people nowadays speak a very different Scots from their grandparents.*"

According to your research, is this an accurate statement?

In your answer you should consider some of the following: vocabulary, grammar, phonology, idiomatic expressions, slang.

Topic D—Uses of Scots in the media

7. "*There is no place for Scots in serious programmes such as news and current affairs.*"

Discuss the extent to which you agree with this statement making reference, where appropriate, to particular media texts.

8. "*The use of Scots in the media adds an extra dimension to entertainment.*"

Discuss this statement with reference to media texts you have studied. You could consider film, television, radio and/or print media.

Topic E—Uses of Scots in contemporary literature

9. Read the following poem carefully and then answer **either** of the questions, (*a*) **or** (*b*), that follow it.

CAN'T SPELL, WON'T SPELL

On hearing of a new Scots computer spellcheck program

Cannae spell, winnae spell—lay it oan thi line:
when it comes tae orthaegraphic skills this laddie disnae shine.
Eh cannae spell "MaGonnagal", Eh cannae spell "Renaissence"—
hoo Eh feel about this flaw is becummin raw complaysance.
5 If Eh cannae spell in English dae Eh huvtue spell in Scots?
Is meh joattur filled wi crosses when thi proablem is wir nots?
Wir not a singul naishun and therr's not a singul tongue:
we talk wan wey gin wir aalder and anither if wir young:
we talk different in thi Borders than we dae up in this Broch;
10 wir meenisters talk funny when they skate oan frozen lochs.
Huv ye seen hoo Lech Walensa's Roabin Williums wi a tash?
Huv ye noticed hoo Pat Lally's kinna nippy wi thi cash?
Well yi widnae if yir sittan wi yir heid stuck til a screen
Trehin tae spell oot whit ye think insteid of seyin whit ye mean.

(Bill Herbert)

(*a*) Compare the use of Scots in this poem with the use of Scots by any other writer you have studied. Comment on the literary and cultural significance of the linguistic choices made by the writers.

OR

(*b*) (i) What issues about the spelling of Scots are raised in this poem?

(ii) Discuss the effectiveness of Bill Herbert's spelling of Scots in the poem.

(iii) From your own study of literature in contemporary Scots, do you agree that "*therr's not a singul tongue*"?

10. The following dramatic extract presents conversation among five characters, Charlie, Hughie, Eddie, Willie and Pat from the Bill Bryden play *Willie Rough*. The play was written in the 1970s and set in the Clyde Shipyards of the 1950s. A strike has been called at the shipyards over shortage of pay and the calling in of foreign labour.

Read the extract carefully.

Consider the range, density and function of the Scots used by the different speakers.

CHARLIE: Excuse me. Have ye seen Willie Rough?

HUGHIE: Yaird gates. Big meetin.

CHARLIE: He tellt me he'd be here.

HUGHIE: He'll no be long. I'm Hughie. This is Eddie.

5 CHARLIE: Charlie McGrath. I'm a friend o Willie's frae Glesga.

EDDIE [*serving*] Yes?

CHARLIE: Have ye got lemonade?

EDDIE: Aye.

HUGHIE: He's got whisky an' aa.

10 CHARLIE: I don't drink.

HUGHIE: How? Was ye an alcoholic or something?

EDDIE: Lea' the fella alane, Hughie. [*He pours lemonade for* CHARLIE]

HUGHIE: There's nae accountin for taste.

CHARLIE [*to* HUGHIE] You have another, Hughie?

15 HUGHIE: That's very kind o ye, Charlie. I'll hav a gless an' a pint.

EDDIE [*pours out another drink*]

CHARLIE: I don't know whether tae go over tae the yard or no.

HUGHIE: You look a bit agitaitit.

CHARLIE: I've got news for Willie. They've downed tools at Weirs o Cathcart. By
20 the end o this week every man on the Clyde'll be out on strike.

EDDIE: Well, don't look sae cheery about it.

HUGHIE: If it's no a war, it's a strike. Is there naething cheery happenin at aa?

EDDIE: Disnae seem like it.

HUGHIE: There's nae point Weirs comin out about the rise. Negotiations havenae
25 broken doun or onything, hav they?

CHARLIE: It's not the rise this time. Shortage of labour.

HUGHIE: Well?

CHARLIE: They've brought engineers over frae America.

HUGHIE: What's wrang wi that?

30 CHARLIE: Skilled men all right, but what dae they do?

HUGHIE: What?

CHARLIE: Return tickets, ten shillings a week more than our own men, an' a guaranteed ten-poun bonus at the end o six months. They've really done it this time. They're skilled men, but they don't know wan end o a
35 discharge-pump frae the other. Willie Rough an' me. We knew they'd make their mistake. We waited. Here it is. Weirs o Cathcart—the bosses themsel's are gonna be instrumental in getting twopence an hour frae Glesga tae the Tail o the Bank!

EDDIE: When, but?

40 HUGHIE: Aye, that's pit your gas at a peep!

CHARLIE: Not at all. Don't you believe it. I've lived for this morning. Can ye no see? War or nae war, this'll show that the unions'll survive. The working man's been the goods and chattels of the employer class for far too long. We're in nae state tae think or even live as human beings. A
45 day like this is to exploit our hatred and kindle it intae rebellion. The day we tell them we're united. Themorra, we frighten them tae death. They can stick the Defence o the Realm Act. From now on they'll have to reckon wi us as a fighting organ of the working classes!

HUGHIE: The Band o Hope!

50 WILLIE *comes in with* PAT *and two other workers*

CHARLIE: Willie.

WILLIE: I thought it was you.

CHARLIE: Have you heard about Weirs?

WILLIE: Aye. I heard.

55 CHARLIE: Well . . . are ye out? Are ye on strike?

WILLIE: Aye.

WILLIE *and* PAT *move over to their table.* CHARLIE *follows.*

CHARLIE: We knew wan o they Toffs would dae somethin' daft, didn't we? A Bell's, Willie?

60 WILLIE: Aye, thanks.

CHARLIE: Pat, you do the needful.

CHARLIE *gives* PAT *some money.* PAT *goes over to the bar.*

PAT: Glass o lemonade an two Bell's, Eddie.

65	HUGHIE:	Eh. Three Bell's. Fairly lashin out, that yin. Mair like a christenin nor a strike.
	PAT:	Wait tae I tell Bernadette.
	HUGHIE:	Nae alternative, tho.
	PAT:	Still, wait tae I tell Bernadette.
	CHARLIE:	It's good news, Willie.
70	WILLIE:	Listen tae me, Charlie McGrath. I've just pit eight hunner men on the street, an' afore the day's out there'll be thousans, an' I don't think that's very good news, so I don't!
	CHARLIE:	But it's the mistake. The clowns have done it. They know where to stick their penny an hour. It's twopence or nothin'.
75, 80	WILLIE:	I wish I wis like you, Charlie. I dae sometimes. Honest. Ye're like that crann over there. Just like steel. Ye don't get that wee tightness in your stomach as if ye were gaunna spew your ring up. Aa mornin, when you've been thinkin about organisation, I've been thinkin about next week or the week aifter, when the excitement wears a bit thin, an' they're dyin tae get back across that street tae make the price o a hauf or a loaf or three eggs. Ye cannae live on the win'.
	CHARLIE:	I thought ye'd be glad, that's aa.
	WILLIE:	Glad? Ye've nae feelings at all, have ye?

Topic F—Uses of Scots in specialised fields

11. The current Cross Party Group for Scots Language at Holyrood has been debating ways to increase the use of Scots in society.

One issue recently debated was the introduction of Scots signage into the Parliamentary building.

"*The Convener wuid write tae the Presidin Officer and ask wha has responsibeelity for signage, and whan deceisions wuid be taen.*" (Minutes 2001)

(*a*) In your opinion, what decisions would need to be taken to introduce Scots language signage into the Parliament at Holyrood? What difficulties may need to be overcome?

(*b*) In what other areas of public life could Scots (including signage) be promoted? Explain your reasons for choosing these areas.

12. Based upon your research into this topic, describe the characteristics of Scots in **one** or **more than one** specialised field you have chosen and account for its survival.

You might consider examples such as Place Names, Street Names, Agriculture, Fishing, the Church, the Law, the Building Trade or any other area about which you have knowledge.

[Turn over

Section 3—Literature

You must answer **one** question only in this section.

You must base your answer only on text(s) **specified by SQA or nominated by your school or college and approved by SQA for Literature.**

Texts specified by SQA may be used to answer **any question** (1–28). Nominated and approved texts may only be used to answer **an alternative question** (23–28).

If you attempt an alternative question (23–28), you must indicate clearly the specified **or** nominated and approved text(s) on which your answer is based.

DRAMA

1. Shakespeare

Examine Shakespeare's dramatic presentation of villainy in **either** or **both** of the specified texts.

2. Chekhov

"*Helpless before the changes taking place in 19th century Russia, the central characters take refuge in elaborate, improbable dreams of renewed prosperity.*"

How far is this statement true of *The Cherry Orchard* **and** *Uncle Vanya*?

3. Shaw

"*In Shaw, all human relationships involve a conflict of wills.*"

Discuss with reference to the central relationships in **each** of the specified texts.

4. Pinter

Examine the uses Pinter makes of uncertainty and ambiguity in **either** *The Caretaker* **or** *The Homecoming*.

5. Stoppard

Show how the element of surprise is a significant aspect of Stoppard's dramatic method in *Rosencrantz and Guildenstern are Dead* **and** *Arcadia*.

6. Lochhead

Evaluate Lochhead's treatment of issues of gender in *Mary Queen of Scots Got Her Head Chopped Off* **and** *Dracula*.

POETRY

7. Chaucer

"*In the General Prologue, only the Knight, the Parson, and the Plowman are treated without any touch of irony at all.*"

How far do you agree?

8. Donne and the metaphysical poets

Basing your answer on **three** or **four** poems, examine the distinctive poetic features of Donne's treatment of secular love.

9. Hopkins

What are the principal poetic means by which Hopkins gives voice to his struggles with God?

10. Plath

"*Plath's poetry is remarkable for its essentially confessional nature—its intensely personal revelation of spiritual and emotional disturbances.*"

Show how Plath makes effective poetry out of such "*intensely personal*" subject matter in **three** or **four** of her poems.

11. Heaney

Read the following extract from *Kinship* and then answer the question that follows it.

II

Quagmire, swampland, morass:
the slime kingdoms,
domains of the cold-blooded,
of mud pads and dirtied eggs.

5 But *bog*
meaning soft,
the fall of windless rain,
pupil of amber.

Ruminant ground,
10 digestion of mollusc
and seed-pod,
deep pollen-bin.

Earth-pantry, bone-vault,
sun-bank, embalmer
15 of votive goods
and sabred fugitives.

Insatiable bride.
Sword-swallower,
casket, midden,
20 floe of history.

Ground that will strip
its dark side,
nesting ground,
outback of my mind.

By detailed analysis of this extract and by making reference to **at least two** other poems, show how Heaney finds significance in "bogland".

12. Dunn

Examine Dunn's treatment of working class experience in **three** or **four** of his poems.

PROSE FICTION

13. Austen

"*In* ***Emma****, the distinctions of hierarchy and rank are scrupulously upheld; in* ***Persuasion****, we are introduced to a much more critical view of the values of birth, rank and place.*"

How far do you agree?

14. Dickens

Discuss Dickens's use of symbolism in *Bleak House* **and/or** in *Great Expectations*.

15. Hardy

How far do you agree that—in *The Mayor of Casterbridge* **and/or** in *Tess of the d'Urbervilles*—"*Hardy shows how human desires and wishes are destined to be crushed underfoot by unthinking and unfeeling authority*"?

16. Joyce

Referring to his choice of setting for his fiction, Joyce said that he chose Dublin because that city seemed to him "*the centre of paralysis*".

Compare and contrast Joyce's treatment of the theme of "*paralysis*" in **either** *A Portrait of the Artist as a Young Man* **or** any **two** or **three** of the stories in *Dubliners*.

17. Spark

"*Spark's fiction is remarkable for the complexity of its narrative structures.*"

Discuss with reference to *The Prime of Miss Jean Brodie* **and** *The Girls of Slender Means*.

18. Achebe

How effectively does Achebe achieve a balanced portrayal of the consequences of the clash of cultures in *Things Fall Apart* **and** *A Man of the People*?

PROSE NON-FICTION

19. Autobiography

Discuss the treatment of the writer's relationship with his or her parents in any **two** of the specified autobiographies.

20. Autobiography

"*All autobiography uses fictional techniques.*"

Analyse and evaluate the fictional techniques employed in any **one** of the specified autobiographies.

21. Travel Writing

How far might it be claimed of any **two** of the specified texts that they are essentially "*journeys of mental and moral discovery*"?

22. Travel Writing

"*For my part, I travel not to go anywhere, but to go. I travel for travel's sake. The great affair is to move.*"

Discuss the effectiveness of any **one** of the specified texts in creating a sense of "*travel for travel's sake*"—a sense of exhilaration at being on the "*move*".

ALTERNATIVE QUESTIONS

23. Drama

In the Introduction to his *Collected Plays* Arthur Miller states that the dramatist must concentrate on developing his or her "*protagonists' social and symbolic roles, rather than their private characteristics*".

Discuss Miller's assertion with reference to the presentation of any **one** dramatist's central characters. You should refer to **two** plays in your answer.

24. Drama

Discuss the uses made of historical material by any **one** dramatist.

In your answer you may refer to **one** or **more than one** play.

25. Poetry

Discuss the uses made of dramatised voices—in monologue or in dialogue—in the work of **one** or **more than one** poet.

In your answer you should refer to **three** or **four** poems.

26. Poetry

"*My poems—I should suppose everyone's poems—are set to trip the reader head foremost into the boundless.*"

(Robert Frost)

Examine the means by which any **one** poet "*trips*" the reader into new experience from which the reader may learn something important.

In your answer you should refer to **three** or **four** poems.

27. Prose fiction

How effectively, in your view, does any **one** novelist explore the effects of social change?

In your answer you should refer to **at least two** novels.

28. Prose fiction

Examine some of the ways by which any **one** novelist conveys the inner experiences, the thoughts, the feelings of his or her characters.

In your answer you should refer to **at least two** novels.

Section 4—Scottish Literature

You must answer **one** question only in this section.

You must base your answer only on text(s) **specified by SQA or nominated by your school or college and approved by SQA for Scottish Literature**.

Texts specified by SQA may be used to answer **any question** (1–28). Nominated and approved texts may only be used to answer **an alternative question** (23–28).

If you attempt an alternative question (23–28), you must indicate clearly the specified **or** nominated and approved text(s) on which your answer is based.

DRAMA

1. Lindsay

Analyse the dramatic impact of the ending of *Ane Satyre of the Thrie Estaitis*.

2. Bridie

"*Bridie's achievement as a dramatist rests on his combination of lightly developed characterisation and beautifully paced plot.*"

How far do you agree?

3. McLellan

In what ways does characterisation contribute to the presentation of theme in *Jamie the Saxt* **and** *The Flouers o Edinburgh?*

4. Byrne

Discuss the effects created by variations of tone in *The Slab Boys Trilogy*.

5. Glover

Discuss the dramatic means by which Glover explores the vulnerability of women in *Bondagers* **and** *The Straw Chair*.

6. Lochhead

Evaluate Lochhead's treatment of issues of gender in *Mary Queen of Scots Got Her Head Chopped Off* **and** *Dracula*.

POETRY

7. Dunbar

Read the following poem carefully and then answer questions (*a*) and (*b*) that follow it (*Page twenty*).

ALL ERDLY JOY RETURNIS IN PANE

OFF LENTREN in the first mornyng,
Airly as did the day up spring,
Thus sang ane bird with voce upplane,
"All erdly joy returnis in pane."

5 "O man! haif mynd that thow mon pas;
Remembir that thow art bot as,
And sall in as return agane:
All erdly joy returnis in pane."

"Haif mynd that eild ay followis yowth;
10 Deth followis lyfe with gaipand mowth,
Devoring fruct and flowring grane:
All erdly joy returnis in pane."

"Welth, warldly gloir, and riche array
Ar all bot thornis laid in thy way,
15 Ourcowerd with flouris laid in ane trane:
All erdly joy returnis in pane."

"Come nevir yit May so fresche and grene,
Bot Januar come als wod and kene;
Wes nevir sic drowth bot anis come rane:
20 All erdly joy returnis in pane."

"Evirmair unto this warldis joy
As nerrest air succeidis noy;
Thairfoir, quhen joy ma nocht remane,
His verry air succeidis pane."

25 "Heir helth returnis in seiknes,
And mirth returnis in havines,
Toun in desert, forrest in plane:
All erdly joy returnis in pane."

"Fredome returnis in wrechitnes,
30 And trewth returnis in dowbilnes,
With fenyeit wordis to mak men fane:
All erdly joy returnis in pane."

[Turn over

"Vertew returnis in to vyce,
And honour in to avaryce;
35 With cuvatyce is consciens slane:
All erdly joy returnis in pane."

"Sen erdly joy abydis nevir,
Wirk for the joy that lestis evir;
For uder joy is all bot vane:
40 All erdly joy returnis in pane."

(*a*) Make a detailed examination of the principal poetic techniques used by Dunbar in this poem.

(*b*) How characteristic are these techniques of Dunbar's moral and religious poetry?

8. The Scottish Ballads

"*There is seldom anything pure about love in the Scottish ballads. It always seems to be contaminated by other strong emotions.*"

Discuss with reference to **three** or **four** traditional Scottish ballads.

9. Fergusson

Analyse Fergusson's portrayal of city life in **two** or **three** poems.

10. Morgan

"*In the beguiling playfulness that characterises many of Morgan's best poems there is often a deeply serious purpose.*"

Discuss with reference to **three** or **four** poems.

11. Dunn

Examine Dunn's treatment of working class experience in **three** or **four** of his poems.

12. Duffy

"*Biting satire, black humour, cutting irony, deft whimsy: Duffy's poetry encompasses a vast range of comic styles and forms.*"

Discuss.

PROSE FICTION

13. Hogg

Examine Hogg's use of Scots in **either** *The Private Memoirs and Confessions of a Justified Sinner* **or two** or **three** short stories.

14. Stevenson

Compare and contrast the nature and function of setting in *The Strange Case of Dr Jekyll and Mr Hyde* **and** *Weir of Hermiston*.

15. Gunn

"*While limited in context, Gunn's novels of Highland experience are in no way parochial . . . .*"

Discuss with reference to *Highland River* **and** *The Silver Darlings*.

16. Spark

"*Spark's fiction is remarkable for the complexity of its narrative structures.*"

Discuss with reference to *The Prime of Miss Jean Brodie* **and** *The Girls of Slender Means*.

17. Gray

Read the following extract from *Lanark* and then answer questions (*a*) and (*b*) that follow it (*Page twenty-two*).

Lanark had been sitting with his head propped on his hands. He said, "You say you are creating me."

"I am."

"Then how can I have experiences you don't know about? You were surprised
5 when I told you what I saw from the aircraft."

"The answer to that is unusually interesting; please attend closely. When *Lanark* is finished (I am calling the work after you) it will be roughly two hundred thousand words and forty chapters long, and divided into books three, one, two and four."

"Why not one, two, three and four?"

10 "I want *Lanark* to be read in one order but eventually thought of in another. It's an old device. Homer, Vergil, Milton and Scott Fitzgerald used it. There will also be a prologue before book one, an interlude in the centre, and an epilogue two or three chapters before the end."

"I thought epilogues came after the end."

15 "Usually, but mine is too important to go there. Though not essential to the plot it provides some comic distraction at a moment when the narrative sorely needs it. And it lets me utter some fine sentiments which I could hardly trust to a mere character. And it contains critical notes which will save research scholars years of toil. In fact my epilogue is so essential that I am working on it with nearly a quarter of the book
20 still unwritten. I am working on it here, just now, in this conversation. But you have had to reach this room by passing through several chapters I haven't clearly imagined yet, so you know details of the story which I don't. Of course I know the broad general outline. That was planned years ago and mustn't be changed. You have come here from my city of destruction, which is rather like Glasgow, to plead before some
25 sort of world parliament in an ideal city based on Edinburgh, or London, or perhaps Paris if I can wangle a grant from the Scottish Arts Council to go there. Tell me, when you were landing this morning, did you see the Eiffel Tower? Or Big Ben? Or a rock with a castle on it?"

"No. Provan is very like—"

30 "Stop! Don't tell me. My fictions often anticipate the experiences they're based upon, but no author should rely on that sort of thing."

Lanark was so agitated that he stood and walked to the window to sort out his thoughts. The author struck him as a slippery person but too vain and garrulous to be impressive. He went back to the bed and said, "How will my story end?"

35 "Catastrophically. The Thaw narrative shows a man dying because he is bad at loving. It is enclosed by your narrative which shows civilization collapsing for the same reason."

"Listen," said Lanark. "I never tried to be a delegate. I never wanted anything but some sunlight, some love, some very ordinary happiness. And every moment I have 40 been thwarted by organizations and things pushing in a different direction, and now I'm nearly an old man and my reasons for living have shrunk to standing up in public and saying a good word for the only people I know. And you tell me that word will be useless! That you have *planned* it to be useless."

"Yes," said the author, nodding eagerly. "Yes, that's right." Lanark gaped down at 45 the foolishly nodding face and suddenly felt it belonged to a horrible ventriloquist's doll. He raised a clenched fist but could not bring himself to strike. He swung round and punched a painting on an easel and both clattered to the floor. He pushed down the other painting beside the door, went to a tall bookcase in a corner and heaved it over. Books cascaded from the upper shelves and it hit the floor with a crash which 50 shook the room. There were long low shelves around the walls holding books, folders, bottles and tubes of paint. With sweeps of his arm he shoved these to the floor, then turned, breathing deeply, and stared at the bed. The author sat there looking distressed, but the paintings and easels were back in their old places, and glancing around Lanark saw the bookcases had returned quietly to the corner and books, 55 folders, bottles and paint were on the shelves again.

"A conjuror!" said Lanark with loathing. "A damned conjuror!"

"Yes," said the conjuror humbly, "I'm sorry. Please sit down and let me explain why the story has to go like this. You can eat while I talk (I'm sure you're hungry) and afterward you can tell me how you think I could be better. Please sit down." The 60 bedside chair was small but comfortably upholstered. A table had appeared beside it with covered dishes on a tray. Lanark felt more exhausted than hungry, but after sitting for a while he removed a cover out of curiosity. There was a bowl beneath of dark red oxtail soup, so taking a spoon he began to eat.

(*a*) Analyse the function of the authorial voice in this extract.

(*b*) How important do you consider authorial voice to be in *Lanark* as a whole?

18. Galloway

Discuss Galloway's treatment of relationships between the sexes in *The Trick is to Keep Breathing* **and** *Foreign Parts*.

PROSE NON-FICTION

19. Autobiography

"*All autobiography is polemical: at its heart there is a purpose to educate and to convince.*"

Discuss with reference to any **two** of the specified Scottish autobiographies.

20. Autobiography

"*In some autobiographies the author can be seen working towards a positive acceptance and understanding of his or her past.*"

How far is this true of any **two** of the specified Scottish autobiographies?

21. Writing about Scotland

Wealthy and poor . . . urban and rural . . . ugly and beautiful . . . island and mainland . . .

Evaluate the effectiveness of the representations of contrasting aspects of Scotland in any **two** of the specified texts.

22. Writing about Scotland

Analyse the means by which any **one** of the writers of the specified texts makes political statements about Scotland.

ALTERNATIVE QUESTIONS

23. Drama

Show how successful any **one** twentieth-century Scottish dramatist has been in deploying the resources of the Scottish language for particular purposes.

You may refer to **one** or **more than one** play in your answer.

24. Drama

Discuss the representation of women in **two** plays by any **one** contemporary Scottish dramatist.

25. Poetry

One critic has claimed that Scottish poetry is at its best when "*confronting issues of universal significance in ways that are uniquely Scottish*".

Discuss with reference to the work of any **one** contemporary Scottish poet.

26. Poetry

Examine the nature and function of satire in the work of any **one** Scottish poet.

27. Prose fiction

"*In every phase of the Scottish novel's history can be seen a fidelity to local truth, to the particulars of communal place and time and, at the same time, an intention to represent national types and whole cultural epochs.*"

How successful, in your view, is any **one** Scottish novelist in achieving a balance between fidelity to local truth and the wider intention suggested in the quotation?

In your answer you may refer to **one** or **more than one** novel.

[Turn over

28. Prose fiction

"*A central preoccupation of novels by Scottish writers is the individual's search for identity in a hostile society.*"

How effectively, in your view, does any **one** Scottish novelist portray "*the individual's search for identity*"?

In your answer you may refer to **one** or **more than one** novel.

Section 5—Textual Analysis

You must answer **one** question only in this section.

1. Prose fiction [*Pages twenty-five to twenty-seven*]

The following extract is from the first chapter of the novel ***Middlemarch*** *(1871) by George Eliot. One of the central characters in the novel is Dorothea Brooke. In this chapter, George Eliot begins to establish the characters of Dorothea Brooke and her younger sister, Celia. At this point in the chapter, the sisters are discussing what to do with the jewels left to them by their mother.*

Read the extract carefully and then answer the question that follows it (Page twenty-seven).

MIDDLEMARCH

Early in the day Dorothea had returned from the infant school which she had set going in the village, and was taking her usual place in the pretty sitting-room which divided the bedrooms of the sisters, bent on finishing a plan for some buildings (a kind of work which she delighted in), when Celia, who had been watching her with a
5 hesitating desire to propose something, said—

"Dorothea dear, if you don't mind—if you are not very busy—suppose we looked at mamma's jewels to-day, and divided them? It is exactly six months to-day since uncle gave them to you, and you have not looked at them yet."

Celia's face had the shadow of a pouting expression in it, the full presence of the
10 pout being kept back by an habitual awe of Dorothea and principle; two associated facts which might show a mysterious electricity if you touched them incautiously. To her relief, Dorothea's eyes were full of laughter as she looked up.

"What a wonderful little almanac you are, Celia! Is it six calendar or six lunar months?"

15 "It is the last day of September now, and it was the first of April when uncle gave them to you. You know, he said that he had forgotten them till then. I believe you have never thought of them since you locked them up in the cabinet here."

"Well, dear, we should never wear them, you know." Dorothea spoke in a full cordial tone, half caressing, half explanatory. She had her pencil in her hand, and was
20 making tiny side-plans on a margin.

Celia coloured, and looked very grave. "I think, dear, we are wanting in respect to mamma's memory, to put them by and take no notice of them. And," she added, after hesitating a little, with a rising sob of mortification, "necklaces are quite usual now; and Madame Poinçon, who was stricter in some things even than you are, used to wear
25 ornaments. And Christians generally—surely there are women in heaven now who wore jewels." Celia was conscious of some mental strength when she really applied herself to argument.

"You would like to wear them?" exclaimed Dorothea, an air of astonished discovery animating her whole person with a dramatic action which she had caught from that
30 very Madame Poinçon who wore the ornaments. "Of course, then, let us have them out. Why did you not tell me before? But the keys, the keys!" She pressed her hands against the sides of her head and seemed to despair of her memory.

"They are here," said Celia, with whom this explanation had been long meditated and prearranged.

35 "Pray open the large drawer of the cabinet and get out the jewel-box."

The casket was soon open before them, and the various jewels spread out, making a bright parterre on the table. It was no great collection, but a few of the ornaments were really of remarkable beauty, the finest that was obvious at first being a necklace of purple amethysts set in exquisite gold work, and a pearl cross with five brilliants in it. Dorothea immediately took up the necklace and fastened it round her sister's neck, where it fitted almost as closely as a bracelet; but the circle suited the Henrietta-Maria style of Celia's head and neck, and she could see that it did, in the pier-glass opposite.

"There, Celia! you can wear that with your Indian muslin. But this cross you must wear with your dark dresses."

Celia was trying not to smile with pleasure. "O Dodo, you must keep the cross yourself."

"No, no, dear, no," said Dorothea, putting up her hand with careless deprecation.

"Yes, indeed you must; it would suit you—in your black dress, now," said Celia, insistingly. "You *might* wear that."

"Not for the world, not for the world. A cross is the last thing I would wear as a trinket." Dorothea shuddered slightly.

"Then you will think it wicked in me to wear it," said Celia, uneasily.

"No, dear, no," said Dorothea, stroking her sister's cheek. "Souls have complexions too: what will suit one will not suit another."

"But you might like to keep it for mamma's sake."

"No, I have other things of mamma's—her sandal-wood box, which I am so fond of—plenty of things. In fact, they are all yours, dear. We need discuss them no longer. There—take away your property."

Celia felt a little hurt. There was a strong assumption of superiority in this Puritanic toleration, hardly less trying to the blond flesh of an unenthusiastic sister than a Puritanic persecution.

"But how can I wear ornaments if you, who are the elder sister, will never wear them?"

"Nay, Celia, that is too much to ask, that I should wear trinkets to keep you in countenance. If I were to put on such a necklace as that, I should feel as if I had been pirouetting. The world would go round with me, and I should not know how to walk."

Celia had unclasped the necklace and drawn it off. "It would be a little tight for your neck; something to lie down and hang would suit you better," she said, with some satisfaction. The complete unfitness of the necklace from all points of view for Dorothea, made Celia happier in taking it. She was opening some ring-boxes, which disclosed a fine emerald with diamonds, and just then the sun passing beyond a cloud sent a bright gleam over the table.

"How very beautiful these gems are!" said Dorothea, under a new current of feeling, as sudden as the gleam. "It is strange how deeply colours seem to penetrate one, like scent. I suppose that is the reason why gems are used as spiritual emblems in the Revelation of St. John. They look like fragments of heaven. I think that emerald is more beautiful than any of them."

"And there is a bracelet to match it," said Celia. "We did not notice this at first."

"They are lovely," said Dorothea, slipping the ring and bracelet on her finely-turned finger and wrist, and holding them towards the window on a level with her eyes. All the while her thought was trying to justify her delight in the colours by merging them in her mystic religious joy.

"You *would* like those, Dorothea," said Celia, rather falteringly, beginning to think with wonder that her sister showed some weakness, and also that emeralds would suit
85 her own complexion even better than purple amethysts. "You must keep that ring and bracelet—if nothing else. But see, these agates are very pretty—and quiet."

"Yes! I will keep these—this ring and bracelet," said Dorothea. Then, letting her hand fall on the table, she said in another tone—"Yet what miserable men find such things, and work at them, and sell them!" She paused again, and Celia thought that her
90 sister was going to renounce the ornaments, as in consistency she ought to do.

"Yes, dear, I will keep these," said Dorothea, decidedly. "But take all the rest away, and the casket."

She took up her pencil without removing the jewels, and still looking at them. She thought of often having them by her, to feed her eye at these little fountains of pure
95 colour.

"Shall you wear them in company?" said Celia, who was watching her with real curiosity as to what she would do.

Dorothea glanced quickly at her sister. Across all her imaginative adornment of those whom she loved, there darted now and then a keen discernment, which was not
100 without a scorching quality. If Miss Brooke* ever attained perfect meekness, it would not be for lack of inward fire.

"Perhaps," she said, rather haughtily. "I cannot tell to what level I may sink."

Celia blushed, and was unhappy; she saw that she had offended her sister, and dared not say even anything pretty about the gift of the ornaments which she put back
105 into the box and carried away. Dorothea too was unhappy, as she went on with her plan-drawing, questioning the purity of her own feeling and speech in the scene which had ended with that little explosion.

Celia's consciousness told her that she had not been at all in the wrong: it was quite natural and justifiable that she should have asked that question, and she repeated
110 to herself that Dorothea was inconsistent: either she should have taken her full share of the jewels, or, after what she had said, she should have renounced them altogether.

"I am sure—at least, I trust," thought Celia, "that the wearing of a necklace will not interfere with my prayers. And I do not see that I should be bound by Dorothea's opinions now we are going into society, though of course she herself ought to be bound
115 by them. But Dorothea is not always consistent."

Thus Celia, mutely bending over her tapestry, until she heard her sister calling her.

"Here, Kitty, come and look at my plan; I shall think I am a great architect, if I have not got incompatible stairs and fireplaces."

120 As Celia bent over the paper, Dorothea put her cheek against her sister's arm caressingly. Celia understood the action. Dorothea saw that she had been in the wrong, and Celia pardoned her. Since they could remember, there had been a mixture of criticism and awe in the attitude of Celia's mind towards her elder sister. The younger had always worn a yoke; but is there any yoked creature without its private
125 opinions?

* ie Dorothea

Question

As she establishes the characters of the two sisters in this extract, by what means does George Eliot guide the reader's responses to them?

2. Prose non-fiction [*Pages twenty-eight to thirty*]

*Read carefully the essay **A Piece of Chalk** (1895) by G. K. Chesterton and then answer the question that follows it (Page thirty).*

I remember one splendid morning, all blue and silver, in the summer holidays, when I reluctantly tore myself away from the task of doing nothing in particular, and put on a hat of some sort and picked up a walking-stick, and put six very bright-coloured chalks in my pocket. I then went into the kitchen (which, along with the rest of the house, 5 belonged to a very square and sensible old woman in a Sussex village), and asked the owner and occupant of the kitchen if she had any brown paper. She had a great deal; in fact, she had too much; and she mistook the purpose and the rationale of the existence of brown paper. She seemed to have an idea that if a person wanted brown paper he must be wanting to tie up parcels; which was the last thing I wanted to do; indeed, it is a 10 thing which I have found to be beyond my mental capacity. Hence she dwelt very much on the varying qualities of toughness and endurance in the material. I explained to her that I only wanted to draw pictures on it, and that I did not want them to endure in the least; and that from my point of view, therefore, it was a question not of tough consistency, but of responsive surface, a thing comparatively irrelevant in a parcel. 15 When she understood that I wanted to draw she offered to overwhelm me with note-paper, apparently supposing that I did my notes and correspondence on old brown paper wrappers from motives of economy.

I then tried to explain the rather delicate logical shade, that I not only liked brown paper, but liked the quality of brownness in paper, just as I liked the quality of 20 brownness in October woods, or in beer, or in the peat-streams of the North. Brown paper represents the primal twilight of the first toil of creation, and with a bright-coloured chalk or two you can pick out points of fire in it, sparks of gold, and blood-red, and sea-green, like the first fierce stars that sprang out of divine darkness. All this I said (in an off-hand way) to the old woman; and I put the brown paper in my pocket 25 along with the chalks, and possibly other things. I suppose every one must have reflected how primeval and how poetical are the things that one carries in one's pocket; the pocket-knife, for instance, the type of all human tools, the infant of the sword. Once I planned to write a book of poems entirely about the things in my pocket. But I found it would be too long; and the age of the great epics is past.

*

30 With my stick and my knife, my chalks and my brown paper, I went out on to the great downs. I crawled across those colossal contours that express the best quality of England, because they are at the same time soft and strong. The smoothness of them has the same meaning as the smoothness of great cart-horses, or the smoothness of the beech-tree; it declares in the teeth of our timid and cruel theories that the mighty are 35 merciful. As my eye swept the landscape, the landscape was as kindly as any of its cottages, but for power it was like an earthquake. The villages in the immense valley were safe, one could see, for centuries; yet the lifting of the whole land was like the lifting of one enormous wave to wash them all away.

I crossed one swell of living turf after another, looking for a place to sit down and
40 draw. Do not, for heaven's sake, imagine I was going to sketch from Nature. I was going to draw devils and seraphim, and blind old gods that men worshipped before the dawn of right, and saints in robes of angry crimson, and seas of strange green, and all the sacred or monstrous symbols that look so well in bright colours on brown paper. They are much better worth drawing than Nature; also they are much easier to draw.
45 When a cow came slouching by in the field next to me, a mere artist might have drawn it; but I always get wrong in the hind legs of quadrupeds. So I drew the soul of the cow; which I saw there plainly walking before me in the sunlight; and the soul was all purple and silver, and had seven horns and the mystery that belongs to all the beasts. But though I could not with a crayon get the best out of the landscape, it does not
50 follow that the landscape was not getting the best out of me. And this, I think, is the mistake that people make about the old poets who lived before Wordsworth, and were supposed not to care very much about Nature because they did not describe it much.

They preferred writing about great men to writing about great hills; but they sat on the great hills to write it. They gave out much less about Nature, but they drank in,
55 perhaps, much more. They painted the white robes of their holy virgins with the blinding snow, at which they had stared all day. They blazoned the shields of their paladins with the purple and gold of many heraldic sunsets. The greenness of a thousand green leaves clustered into the live green figure of Robin Hood. The blueness of a score of forgotten skies became the blue robes of the Virgin. The
60 inspiration went in like sunbeams and came out like Apollo.

*

But as I sat scrawling these silly figures on the brown paper, it began to dawn on me, to my great disgust, that I had left one chalk, and that a most exquisite and essential chalk, behind. I searched all my pockets, but I could not find any white chalk. Now, those who are acquainted with all the philosophy (nay, religion) which is typified
65 in the art of drawing on brown paper, know that white is positive and essential. I cannot avoid remarking here upon a moral significance. One of the wise and awful truths which this brown-paper art reveals, is that, that white is a colour. It is not a mere absence of colour; it is a shining and affirmative thing, as fierce as red, as definite as black. When (so to speak) your pencil grows red-hot, it draws roses; when it grows
70 white-hot, it draws stars. And one of the two or three defiant verities of the best religious morality, of real Christianity for example, is exactly the same thing; the chief assertion of religious morality is that white is a colour. Virtue is not the absence of vices or the avoidance of moral dangers; virtue is a vivid and separate thing, like pain or a particular smell. Mercy does not mean not being cruel or sparing people revenge
75 or punishment; it means a plain and positive thing like the sun, which one has either seen or not seen. Chastity does not mean abstention from sexual wrong; it means something flaming, like Joan of Arc. In a word, God paints in many colours; but He never paints so gorgeously, I had almost said so gaudily, as when He paints in white. In a sense our age has realized this fact, and expressed it in our sullen costume. For if it
80 were really true that white was a blank and colourless thing, negative and non-committal, then white would be used instead of black and grey for the funeral dress of this pessimistic period. We should see city gentlemen in frock coats of spotless silver satin, with top hats as white as wonderful arum lilies. Which is not the case.

Meanwhile I could not find my chalk.

[Turn over

*

85 I sat on the hill in a sort of despair. There was no town nearer than Chichester at which it was even remotely probable that there would be such a thing as an artist's colourman. And yet, without white, my absurd little pictures would be as pointless as the world would be if there were no good people in it. I stared stupidly round, racking my brain for expedients. Then I suddenly stood up and roared with laughter, again 90 and again, so that the cows stared at me and called a committee. Imagine a man in the Sahara regretting that he had no sand for his hour-glass. Imagine a gentleman in mid-ocean wishing that he had brought some salt water with him for his chemical experiments. I was sitting on an immense warehouse of white chalk. The landscape was made entirely out of white chalk. White chalk was piled mere miles until it met 95 the sky. I stooped and broke a piece off the rock I sat on: it did not mark so well as the shop chalks do; but it gave the effect. And I stood there in a trance of pleasure, realizing that this Southern England is not only a grand peninsula, and a tradition and civilization; it is something even more admirable. It is a piece of chalk.

Question

"*Behind the playful style of Chesterton's essays often lies a seriousness of purpose.*"

How far do you find this statement true of ***A Piece of Chalk***?

3. Poetry [*Page thirty-one*]

*Read carefully the poem **Unwittingly** by John Burnside and then answer the question that follows it.*

UNWITTINGLY

I've visited the place
where thought begins:
pear trees suspended in sunlight, narrow shops,
alleys to nothing
5 but nettles
and broken wars;
and though it might look different
to you:

a seaside town, with steep roofs
10 the colour of oysters,
the corner of some junkyard with its glint
of coming rain,

though someone else again would recognise
the warm barn, the smell of milk,
15 the wintered cattle
shifting in the dark,

it's always the same lit space,
the one good measure:
Sometimes you'll wake in a chair
20 as the light is fading,

or stop on the way to work
as a current of starlings
turns on itself
and settles above the green,

25 and because what we learn in the dark
remains all our lives,
a noise like the sea, displacing the day's
pale knowledge,

you'll come to yourself
30 in a glimmer of rainfall or frost,
the burnt smell of autumn,
a meeting of parallel lines,

and know you were someone else
for the longest time,
35 pretending you knew where you were, like a diffident tourist,
lost on the one main square, and afraid to enquire.

Question

Write a critical commentary on the poem.

In your commentary you should:

- analyse the techniques used by the poet in lines 1–18 to give significance to

  ". . . the place
  where thought begins"

- make a detailed study of lines 19–36—giving particular attention to what is suggested by the following:

  ". . . because what we learn in the dark
  remains . . .
  you'll come to yourself . . .
  and know you were someone else
  for the longest time,
  pretending . . ."

- comment on the importance of the title and of any other features of the poem you think relevant.

4. Drama [*Pages thirty-two to thirty-seven*]

The following extract is the end of **Roots** *(1959) by Arnold Wesker. Beatie, a young woman of 22, has returned for two weeks to her family home in rural Norfolk. She has been waiting for the arrival of Ronnie, her partner of three years.*

Beatie is the main character in this extract. Other characters (in order of appearance) are:

PEARL:	*Beatie's sister-in-law*
MRS BRYANT:	*Beatie's mother*
MR BRYANT:	*Beatie's father*
JENNY:	*Beatie's sister*
FRANK:	*Beatie's brother*
JIMMY:	*Beatie's brother-in-law*

Read the extract carefully and then answer the question that follows it (Page thirty-seven).

[*There is a knock on the front door.*]

BEATIE: [*jumping down joyously*] He's here, he's here! [*But at the door it is the* POSTMAN, *from whom she takes a letter and a parcel.*] Oh, the silly fool, the fool. Trust him to write a letter on the day he's coming.
5 Parcel for you Mother.

PEARL: Oh, that'll be your dress from the club.

MRS BRYANT: What dress is this then? I didn't ask for no dress from the club.

PEARL: Yes you did, you did ask me, didn't she ask me Frank? Why, we were looking through the book together Mother.

10 MRS BRYANT: No matters what we was doin' together I aren't hevin' it.

PEARL: But Mother you distinctly—

MRS BRYANT: I aren't hevin' it so there now!

[BEATIE *has read the letter—the contents stun her. She cannot move. She stares around speechlessly at everyone.*]

15 MRS BRYANT: Well, what's the matter wi' you gal? Let's have a read. [*Takes letter and reads contents in a dead flat but loud voice—as though it were a proclamation*] "My dear Beatie. It wouldn't really work would it? My ideas about handing on a new kind of life are quite useless and romantic if I'm really honest. If I were a healthy human being it
20 might have been all right but most of us intellectuals are pretty sick and neurotic—as you have often observed—and we couldn't build a world even if we were given the reins of government—not yet any-rate. I don't blame you for being stubborn, I don't blame you for ignoring every suggestion I ever made—I only blame myself for
25 encouraging you to believe we could make a go of it and now two weeks of your not being here has given me the cowardly chance to think about it and decide and I—"

BEATIE: [*snatching letter*] Shut up!

MRS BRYANT: Oh—so we know now do we?

30 MR BRYANT: What's this then—ent he comin'?

MRS BRYANT: Yes, we know now.

MR BRYANT: Ent he comin' I ask? BEATIE: *No he ent comin'.*

[*An awful silence ensues. Everyone looks uncomfortable.*]

JENNY: [*softly*] Well blust gal, didn't you know this was going to happen?

35 [BEATIE *shakes her head.*]

MRS BRYANT: So *we're* stubborn are we?

JENNY: Shut you up Mother, the girl's upset.

MRS BRYANT: Well I can see that, I can see that, he ent coming, I can see that, and we're here like bloody fools, I can see that.

40 PEARL: Well did you quarrel all that much Beatie?

BEATIE: [*as if discovering this for the first time*] He always wanted me to help him but I never could. Once he tried to teach me to type but soon ever I made a mistake I'd give up. I'd give up every time! I couldn't bear making mistakes. I don't know why, but I couldn't bear making
45 mistakes.

MRS BRYANT: Oh—so we're hearin' the other side o' the story now are we?

BEATIE: He used to suggest I start to copy real objects on to my paintings instead of only abstracts and I never took heed.

MRS BRYANT: Oh, so you never took heed.

50 JENNY: Shut you up I say.

BEATIE: He gimme a book sometimes and I never bothered to read it.

FRANK: [*not maliciously*] What about all this discussion we heard of?

BEATIE: I *never* discussed things. He used to beg me to discuss things but I never saw the point on it.

55 PEARL: And he got riled because o' that?

BEATIE: [*trying to understand*] I didn't have any patience.

MRS BRYANT: Now it's coming out.

BEATIE: I couldn't help him—I never knew patience. Once he looked at me with terrified eyes and said, "We've been together for three years but
60 you don't know who I am or what I'm trying to say—and you don't care do you?"

MRS BRYANT: And there she was tellin' me.

BEATIE: I never knew what he wanted—I didn't think it mattered.

MR BRYANT: And there she were gettin' us to solve the moral problem and now we
65 know she didn't even do it herself. That's a rum 'un, ent it?

MRS BRYANT: The apple don't fall far from the tree—that it don't.

BEATIE: [*wearily*] So you're proud on it? You sit there smug and you're proud that a daughter of yours wasn't able to help her boy friend? Look at you. All of you. You can't say anything. You can't even help your
70 own flesh and blood. Your daughter's bin ditched. It's your problem as well isn't it? I'm part of your family aren't I? Well, help me then! Give me words of comfort! Talk to me—for God's sake, someone talk to me. [*She cries at last.*]

MR BRYANT: Well, what do we do now?

75 MRS BRYANT: We sit down and we eat that's what we do now.

JENNY: Don't be soft Mother, we can't leave the girl crying like that.

MRS BRYANT: Well, blust, 'tent my fault she's cryin'. I did what I could—I prepared all this food, I'd've treated him as my own son if he'd come but he hevn't! We got a whole family gathering specially to greet him,
80 all on us look, but he hevn't come. So what am I supposed to do?

BEATIE: My God, Mother, I hate you—the only thing I ever wanted and I weren't able to keep him, I didn't know how. I hate you, I hate . . .

[MRS BRYANT *slaps Beatie's face. Everyone is a little shocked at this harsh treatment.*]

85 MRS BRYANT: There! I hed enough!

MR BRYANT: Well what d'you wanna do that for?

MRS BRYANT: I hed enough. All this time she've bin home she've bin tellin' me I didn't do this and I didn't do that and I hevn't understood half what she've said and I've hed enough. She talk about bein' part o' the
90 family but she've never lived at home since she've left school look. Then she go away from here and fill her head wi' high-class squit and then it turn out she don't understand any on it herself. It turn out she do just the same things she say I do. [*Into Beatie's face*] Well, am I right gal? I'm right ent I? When you tell me I was stubborn, what
95 you mean was that *he* told you *you* was stubborn—eh? When you tell me I don't understand you mean *you* don't understand isn't it? When you tell me I don't make no effort you mean *you* don't make no effort. Well, what you blaming me for? Blaming me all the time! I haven't bin responsible for you since you left home—you bin on your own.
100 She think I like it, she do! Thinks I like it being cooped up in this house all day. Well I'm telling you my gal—I don't! There! And if I had a chance to be away working somewhere the whole lot on you's could go to hell—the lot on you's. All right so I am a bloody fool—all right! So I know it! A whole two weeks I've bin told it. Well, so then
105 I can't help you my gal, no that I can't, and you get used to that once and for all.

BEATIE: No you can't Mother, I know you can't.

MRS BRYANT: I suppose doin' all those things for him weren't enough. I suppose he weren't satisfied wi' goodness only.

110 BEATIE: Oh, what's the use.

MRS BRYANT: Well, don't you sit there an' sigh gal like you was Lady Nevershit. I ask you something. Answer me. You do the talking then. Go on—you say you know something we don't so *you* do the talking. Talk—go on, talk gal.

115 BEATIE: [*despairingly*] I can't Mother, you're right—the apple don't fall far from the tree do it? You're right, I'm like you. Stubborn, empty, wi' no tools for livin'. I got no roots in nothing. I come from a family o' farm labourers yet I ent got no roots—just like town people—just a mass o' nothin'.

120 FRANK: Roots, gal? What do you mean, roots?

BEATIE: [*impatiently*] Roots, roots, roots! Christ, Frankie, you're in the fields all day, you should know about growing things. Roots! The things you come from, the things that feed you. The things that make you proud of yourself—roots!

125 MR BRYANT: You got a family ent you?

BEATIE: I am not talking about family roots—I mean—the—I mean—Look! Ever since it begun the world's bin growin' hasn't it? Things hev happened, things have bin discovered, people have bin thinking and improving and inventing but what do we know about it all?

130 JIMMY: What is she on about?

BEATIE: [*various interjections*] What do you mean, what am I on about? I'm talking! Listen to me! I'm tellin' you that the world's bin growing for two thousand years and we hevn't noticed it. I'm telling you that we don't know what we are or where we come from. I'm telling you
135 something's cut us off from the beginning. I'm telling you we've got no roots. Blimey Joe! We've all got large allotments, we all grow things around us so we should know about roots. You know how to keep your flowers alive don't you Mother? Jimmy—you know how to keep the roots of your veges strong and healthy. It's not only the corn
140 that need strong roots, you know, it's us too. But what've we got? Go on, tell me, what've we got? We don't know where we push up from and we don't bother neither.

PEARL: Well, I aren't grumbling.

BEATIE: You say you aren't—oh yes, you say so, but look at you. What've you
145 done since you come in? Hev you said anythin'? I mean really said or done anything to show you're alive? Alive! Blust, what do it mean? Do you know what it mean? Any of you? Shall I tell you what Susie said when I went and saw her? She say she don't care if that ole atom bomb drop and she die—that's what she say. And you know why she
150 say it? I'll tell you why, because if she had to care she'd have to do something about it and she find *that* too much effort. Yes she do. She can't be bothered—she's too bored with it all. That's what we all are—we're all too bored.

MRS BRYANT: Blust woman—bored you say, bored? You say Susie's bored, with a
155 radio and television an' that? I go t'hell if she's bored!

BEATIE: Oh yes, we turn on a radio or a TV set maybe, or we go to the pictures—if them's love stories or gangsters—but isn't that the easiest way out? Anything so long as we don't have to make an effort. Well, am I right? You know I'm right. Education ent only books and
160 music—it's asking questions, all the time. There are millions of us, all over the country, and no one, not one of us, is asking questions, we're all taking the easiest way out. Everyone I ever worked with took the easiest way out. We don't fight for anything, we're so mentally lazy we might as well be dead. Blust, we are dead! And you
165 know what Ronnie say sometimes? He say it serves us right! That's what he say—it's our own bloody fault!

JIMMY: So that's us summed up then—so we know where *we* are then!

MRS BRYANT: Well if he don't reckon we count nor nothin', then it's as well he didn't come. There! It's as well he didn't come.

170 BEATIE: Oh, *he* thinks we count all right—living in mystic communion with nature. Living in mystic bloody communion with nature (indeed). But us count? Count Mother? I wonder. Do we? Do you think we really count? You don' wanna take any notice of what them ole papers say about the workers bein' all-important these days—that's
175 all squit! 'Cos we aren't. Do you think when the really talented people in the country get to work they get to work for us? Hell if they do! Do you think they don't know we 'ont make the effort? The writers don't write thinkin' we can understand, nor the painters don't paint expecting us to be interested—that they don't, nor don't the
180 composers give out music thinking we can appreciate it. "Blust," they say, "the masses is too stupid for us to come down to them. Blust," they say, "if they don't make no effort why should we bother?" So you know who come along? The slop singers and the pop writers and the film makers and women's magazines and the
185 Sunday papers and the picture strip love stories—that's who come along, and you don't have to make no effort for them, it come easy. "We know where the money lie," they say, "hell we do! The workers've got it so let's give them what they want. If they want slop songs and film idols we'll give 'em that then. If they want words of
190 one syllable, we'll give 'em that then. If they want the third-rate, *blust*! We'll give 'em that then. Anything's good enough for them 'cos they don't ask for no more!" The whole stinkin' commercial world insults us and we don't care a damn. Well, Ronnie's right—it's our own bloody fault. We want the third-rate—we got it! We got it!
195 We got it! We . . .

[*Suddenly* BEATIE *stops as if listening to herself. She pauses, turns with an ecstatic smile on her face*—]

D'you hear that? D'you hear it? Did you listen to me? I'm talking. Jenny, Frankie, Mother—I'm not quoting no more.

200 MRS BRYANT: [*getting up to sit at table*] Oh hell, I hed enough of her—let her talk a while she'll soon get fed up.

[*The others join her at the table and proceed to eat and murmur.*]

BEATIE: Listen to me someone. [*As though a vision were revealed to her*] God in heaven, *Ronnie*! It does work, it's happening to me, I can feel it's
205 happened, I'm beginning, on my own two feet—I'm beginning . . .

[*The murmur of the family sitting down to eat grows as* BEATIE'S *last cry is heard. Whatever she will do they will continue to live as before. As* BEATIE *stands alone, articulate at last—*]

THE CURTAIN FALLS

Question

Make a detailed study of the means employed by Wesker in the extract to bring the audience to an understanding of the attitudes and positions adopted by Beatie and by members of her family at the end of the play.

In your answer, you should consider:

- the reactions of Beatie, Mrs Bryant and the other characters to the reading of the letter
- the presentation of the relationship between Beatie and her mother
- the imagery and symbolism of "roots".

[Turn over

Section 6—Reading the Media

You must answer **one question only** in this section.

Category A—Film

1. With reference to **at least two** films by the same director, analyse some of the cinematic techniques used by that director to create a personal style.

2. "*Film narrative needs a high level of predictability with just enough variation to surprise and delight the audience.*"

   Discuss with reference to the narrative of **one** or **more than one** film you have studied.

Category B—Television

3. "*Storytelling is at the heart of all television.*"

   With reference to specific examples, show how storytelling techniques are used in any **two** television genres—one **factual** and one **fictional**.

4. "*Ideas about gender obtained through television are very much a construction.*"

   Discuss the means by which ideas about gender are constructed in **one** or **more than one** television programme or series of programmes.

Category C—Radio

5. "*In radio drama, speech is the principal means of creating character.*"

   Discuss the role of speech in creating character in **one** or **more than one** radio drama.

6. "*Each radio channel has a distinctive identity or 'stationality', which is established through its programme content and the way it addresses its audiences.*"

   Discuss with reference to any **one** radio channel—national, regional or local.

Category D—Print journalism

7. "*By choosing to handle certain stories in certain ways, each newspaper presents to its target audience a partial view of the world.*"

   How far do you agree?

   You may refer to **one** or **more than one** newspaper in your answer.

8. Compare and contrast the treatment of a recent political, social or economic issue by **two** different newspapers.

   You may wish to consider aspects such as readership assumptions, language choice, journalistic principles, news values.

Category E—Advertising

9. "*Advertisements target their audience on the basis of feelings like guilt, dissatisfaction, anxiety, inadequacy.*"

By referring to a range of advertisements—or to an advertising campaign—discuss some of the means by which advertisers offer positive solutions to negative feelings.

10. For this question you are provided with two advertisements:

PRADA (from *The Observer Fashion Supplement*, October 2002) (*Page forty*)
HARRIS (from *The Independent on Sunday*, October 2002) (*Page forty-one*)

How effectively do these advertisements convey the messages of the advertisers? In your answer you should consider:

- the use of technical codes to give prominence to the product in each, particularly the use of horizontal, vertical and diagonal lines in the composition
- the cultural codes which establish the representation of the female subject and the setting in the PRADA advertisement
- the written text, both content and typography, in the HARRIS advertisement
- how the qualities of each product are incorporated into the narrative of each advertisement
- assumptions made about audience knowledge of film and film genre.

[Turn over

PRADA
Prada Tel +44 207 399 2030

BY APPOINTMENT TO
H.M. QUEEN ELIZABETH II
MANUFACTURERS OF PAINT BRUSHES
AND PAINTERS TOOLS
L.G. HARRIS & CO. LIMITED,
STOKE PRIOR

Harris no-loss

100% GUARANTEED NO BRISTLE LOSS FOR LIFE - YOU'D BE CRAZY NOT TO USE ONE

[*END OF QUESTION PAPER*]

[BLANK PAGE]

2004 | Advanced Higher

[BLANK PAGE]

X115/701

NATIONAL QUALIFICATIONS 2004

FRIDAY, 14 MAY
1.00 PM – 4.00 PM

ENGLISH
ADVANCED HIGHER

There are four sections in this paper.

Depending on the options you have chosen, you must answer **one** or **two** questions.

If you have submitted a Creative Writing folio, you must answer only **one** question.

Otherwise, you must answer **two** questions.

If you are required to answer only **one question**

- it must be taken from **Section 1—Literary Study**
- you must leave the examination room **after 1 hour 30 minutes**.

If you are required to answer **two questions**

- your first must be taken from **Section 1—Literary Study**
- your second must be taken from **a different section**
- each answer must be written in **a separate answer booklet**
- the maximum time allowed for any question is **1 hour 30 minutes**.

You must identify each question you attempt by indicating clearly

- **the title of the section** from which the question has been taken
- **the number of the question** within that section.

You must also write inside the front cover of your Literary Study answer booklet

- **the topic** of your Specialist Study
- **the texts** used in your Specialist Study.

Section 1—Literary Study

This section is **mandatory** for all candidates.

You must answer **one question only** in this section.

DRAMA

1. Bridie

Read carefully the following extract from Act I of ***The Anatomist*** *and then answer questions (a) and (b) that follow it (Page four).*

MARY: Dr. Knox, you appear to find this situation humorous. I find it humiliating. Walter tells me that this occupation which keeps us apart is God's work. You tell me he is play-acting when he says so. You have answered my question with jeers. I don't understand. I *must* understand. Won't you tell me what you mean? (5)

KNOX: My dear, we all seek to explain ourselves in big words and windy notions. The wise disregard these things. Our friend Walter has a sacred thirst of which he is only half-conscious. The vulgarian, the quack and the theologian are confronted with the Universe. They at once begin to talk and talk and talk. They have no curiosity. They know all about it. They build a mean structure of foolish words and phrases, and say to us, "This is the World." The comparative anatomist *has* curiosity. He institutes a divine search for facts. He is unconcerned with explanations and theories. In time, when you and I are dead, his facts will be collected and their sum will be the Truth. Truth that will show the noblest thing in creation, how to live. Truth that will shatter the idol Mumbo Jumbo, before which man daily debases his magnificence. Truth . . . (10, 15)

MARY: No doubt that is very fine. But it is all words, too.

KNOX: It is a religion. It is a passion.

MARY: It is a very horrid sort of religion. (20)

KNOX: My dear young lady, it is less horrid than the religions of most of mankind. It has its martyrs, it has its heresy-hunts, but its hands are clean of the blood of the innocent.

MARY: Are they?

KNOX: Of course they are. (25)

MARY: Do you call the hands of a resurrectionist clean?

KNOX: Of the blood of the innocent.

MARY: Grave-robbing is worse than murder.

KNOX: Madam, with all respect, you are a pagan atheist to say so. If you believed
30 in an immortal soul, why should you venerate the empty shell it has spurned in its upward flight? And with a false veneration, too. The anatomist alone has a true reverence for the human body. He loves it. He knows it.

MARY: He pays ruffians to tear it from the grave where loving hands have laid it.
35 Your friend Mr. Liston, the surgeon, goes himself and beats the guardians, like the pot-house bully he is.

KNOX: Bob Liston is no friend of mine. I abhor his methods.

MARY: Where do *you* get your bodies from?

KNOX: How should I know? My duty is to teach.

40 [*A pause.*]

MARY: Ah!

KNOX: My child . . . [*He tries to take her hands.*] You love my friend. To love is to understand. Try to understand that he is doing great things, of which not the least is to sacrifice a part of his happiness.

45 WALTER: Mary . . .

MARY: Mr. Anderson, your presence here is inexpressibly painful to me. I am greatly obliged to Dr. Knox for his attempt to put me in the wrong. But he has only convinced me how right I am. I cannot look at one of the three of you without a shudder. I feel as if you had lifted a lid and showed
50 me a glimpse of unspeakable things. Will you excuse me? I'll retire.

AMELIA: Oh, darling, darling!

WALTER: Then that's the end. You can go to hell. If you want me you'll find me in the gutter!

[*He dashes rudely out.*]

55 KNOX: Mr. Raby, perhaps it would be well if you followed him to his gutter and exercised a restraining supervision on his wallowing.

RABY: Eh? I don't quite follow, sir.

KNOX: Go after him and see he comes to no harm. I cannot afford to lose a good assistant.

60 RABY: Very well, sir. Good-night, ma'am, and thank you very much for a pleasant evening. Good-night, ma'am. Good-night, sir.

[*He bows himself out.*]

[Turn over

KNOX: And God's benison on you, sir. . . .

"'To arms! to arms!' the fierce virago cries,
65 And swift as lightning to the combat flies.
All side in parties, and begin the attack;
Fans clap, silks rustle, and tough whalebones crack.
Heroes' and Heroines' shouts confusedly rise,
And bass and treble voices strike the skies.
70 No common weapons in their hands . . ."

MARY: Mr. Knox!

KNOX: "No common weapons . . ."

MARY: Mr. Knox, it is the common talk of this town that you are generally admired by persons of our sex. And this in spite of your hideous face and
75 cynical, filthy, scandalous tongue. There is one lady who does not share their admiration. She loathes and detests and abhors you and all your ways. And she wishes you a very good-night.

[*Exit MARY.*]

KNOX: Poor things. Poor hearts.

80 AMELIA: Your sentiment rings abominably false, Dr. Knox.

KNOX: False, Miss Amelia! I have never in my life been accused . . . Well, perhaps it does. What does it matter?

AMELIA: My sister's happiness matters to me a very great deal. And Walter's too.

KNOX: I did my best, Miss Amelia. But we who are groping among the roots of
85 life cannot be expected to take too seriously the whimsies of the creatures of the air. You are crying! You mustn't cry. It congests the conjunctival sac. Let us consult Schubert. Let us hear what Rossini has to say on the quarrels of lovers. Come.

AMELIA: Ah, no. I couldn't play for you to-night, Doctor.

90 KNOX: I insist. Look—

"I attempt from love's sickness to fly in vain."

Strike up!

[*He begins to play, extremely badly, on his flute. MISS AMELIA struggles helplessly with laughter, tears and his accompaniment.*]

CURTAIN

Questions

(*a*) Analyse, in detail, the means by which in this extract Bridie dramatises Knox's passion for his role as anatomist.

(*b*) How effectively is intensity of passion dramatised in *The Anatomist* as a whole **and** in *Mr Bolfry*?

2. Byrne

Analyse the dramatic means by which Byrne creates tension between hope and despair in *The Slab Boys Trilogy*.

3. Chekhov

Show how the juxtaposition of pathos and the ridiculous is a significant aspect of Chekhov's dramatic method.

4. Glover

Compare and contrast Glover's handling of dramatic structure in *Bondagers* **and** *The Straw Chair*.

5. Lindsay

Discuss the function and the impact of some of Lindsay's satirical techniques in *Ane Satyre of the Thrie Estaitis*.

6. Lochhead

How central is the theme of empowerment of women in *Mary Queen of Scots Got Her Head Chopped Off* **and** in *Dracula*?

7. McLellan

Evaluate the success of McLellan's dramatic representation of the nuances of Scots social behaviour and the oddities of Scots characters in *Jamie the Saxt* **and** in *The Flouers o Edinburgh*.

8. Pinter

Discuss the significance of the intruder figure in *The Caretaker* **and** in *The Homecoming*.

9. Shakespeare

(*a*) "*There's a special providence in the fall of a sparrow. If it be now, 'tis not to come; if it be not to come, it will be now; if it be not now, yet it will come. The readiness is all.*"

How far do Hamlet's words here mark a turning-point in the play?

OR

(*b*) "*As flies to wanton boys, are we to the gods;*
They kill us for their sport."

How important is Gloucester's assertion here to your understanding of *King Lear*?

OR

(*c*) How far do you consider the tragic outcomes of **both** *Hamlet* **and** *King Lear* to be inevitable?

[Turn over

10. Shaw

In his Preface to *Major Barbara*, Shaw says that he is concerned with "*the tragic-comic irony of the conflict between real life and the romantic imagination*".

How far is such a concern apparent in *Major Barbara* **and** in *St Joan*?

11. Stoppard

"*Although many of the ingredients of his drama belong to farce or comedy of manners, behind Stoppard's lightness of approach lies a fundamental seriousness.*"

How far do you agree?

12. Williams

Discuss the contribution of symbolic effects in stage setting, in music, in lighting and in properties to your understanding of *The Glass Menagerie* **and** *A Streetcar Named Desire.*

POETRY

13. Chaucer

Examine the principal means by which Chaucer creates in the Pardoner a character who not only is fraudulent but who also relishes his own fraudulence.

In your answer you should refer both to the *General Prologue* and to the *Pardoner's Prologue and Tale*.

14. Coleridge

Discuss Coleridge's use of symbolism in **three** or **four** poems.

15. Donne and the metaphysical poets

"*Argument and persuasion, and the use of the conceit as their instrument, are the essential elements of metaphysical poetry.*"

Evaluate the effectiveness of **three** or **four** metaphysical poems in the light of this statement.

16. Duffy

Analyse the means by which Duffy explores aspects of childhood and early youth in **three** or **four** poems.

17. Dunbar

Discuss Dunbar's evocation of the pains and the pleasures of human existence in **three** or **four** poems.

18. Dunn

Read the following poem and then answer the question that follows it.

THE HUNCHED

They will not leave me, the lives of other people.
I wear them near my eyes like spectacles.
Sullen magnates, hunched into chins and overcoats
In the back seats of their large cars;
5 Scholars, so conscientious, as if to escape
Things too real, names too easily read,
Preferring language stuffed with difficulties;
And children, furtive with their own parts;
A lonely glutton in the sunlit corner
10 Of an empty Chinese restaurant;
A coughing woman, leaning on a wall,
Her wedding-ring finger in her son's cold hand,
In her back the invisible arch of death.
What makes them laugh, who lives with them?

15 I stooped to lace a shoe, and they all came back,
Mysterious people without names or faces,
Whose lives I guess about, whose dangers tease.
And not one of them has anything at all to do with me.

Analyse the means by which Dunn gives significance to the lives of "*other people*" in this poem **and** in **two** or **three** other poems.

19. Fergusson

It has been said of Fergusson's poetry that "*it displays both a sternly moralistic condemnation of sin and a warmly humane affection for the sinner*".

How far do you agree?

20. Heaney

Drawing evidence from **three** or **four** poems, show how Heaney "*makes remarkable poetry out of apparently unremarkable incidents*".

21. Hopkins

"*Terror rather than beauty lies at the heart of Hopkins's poetry.*"

Examine **three** or **four** of Hopkins's poems in the light of this assertion.

22. Morgan

"*As a poet, Morgan is at his best when throwing fresh light upon the minutiae of everyday experience.*"

How far do you agree?

23. Plath

Analyse and evaluate the effectiveness of the techniques used by Plath to explore aspects of love in **three** or **four** poems.

24. The Scottish Ballads

Analyse the nature and function of the narrative techniques employed in **three** or **four** Scottish ballads.

PROSE FICTION

25. Achebe

"*Achebe avoids presenting the past as idealised and the present as ugly and unsatisfactory.*"

How far do you agree?

You should support your answer with evidence drawn from *Things Fall Apart* **and** *A Man of the People.*

26. Austen

Evaluate the contribution to central thematic concerns of Harriet Smith and Jane Fairfax in *Emma* **and** Mrs Clay and Louisa Musgrove in *Persuasion.*

27. Dickens

Examine Dickens's treatment of corruption in *Great Expectations* **or** in *Bleak House* **or** in both.

28. Forster

Examine Forster's treatment of conflict in *Howards End* **or** in *A Passage To India* ***or*** in both.

29. Galloway

Discuss some of the means by which Galloway represents human vulnerability as a theme in *The Trick is to Keep Breathing* **and** in *Foreign Parts.*

30. Gray

Discuss the nature and function of the comic effects achieved in *Lanark* **and/or** in *Poor Things.*

31. Gunn

"*In his fiction, Gunn uses the past primarily as a means of discovering truths of relevance to the present.*"

How far do you feel this to be true of *Highland River* **and** *The Silver Darlings*?

32. Hardy

Read the following extract from ***Tess of the d'Urbervilles*** *and then answer the question that follows it.*

It was a typical summer evening in June, the atmosphere being in such delicate equilibrium and so transmissive that inanimate objects seemed endowed with two or three senses, if not five. There was no distinction between the near and the far, and an auditor felt close to everything within the horizon. The soundlessness impressed her
5 as a positive entity rather than as the mere negation of noise. It was broken by the strumming of strings.

Tess had heard these notes in the attic above her head. Dim, flattened, constrained by their confinement, they had never appealed to her as now, when they wandered into the still air with a stark quality like that of nudity. To speak absolutely, both
10 instrument and execution were poor; but the relative is all, and as she listened Tess, like a fascinated bird, could not leave the spot. Far from leaving, she drew up towards the performer, keeping behind the hedge that he might not guess her presence.

The outskirt of the garden in which Tess found herself had been left uncultivated for some years, and was now damp and rank with juicy grass which sent up mists of
15 pollen at a touch; and with tall blooming weeds emitting offensive smells — weeds whose red and yellow and purple hues formed a polychrome as dazzling as that of cultivated flowers. She went stealthily as a cat through this profusion of growth, gathering cuckoo-spittle on her skirts, cracking snails that were underfoot, staining her hands with thistle-milk and slug-slime, and rubbing off upon her naked arms sticky
20 blights which, though snow-white on the apple-tree trunks, made madder stains on her skin; thus she drew quite near to Clare, still unobserved of him.

Tess was conscious of neither time nor space. The exaltation which she had described as being producible at will by gazing at a star, came now without any determination of hers; she undulated upon the thin notes of the second-hand harp, and
25 their harmonies passed like breezes through her, bringing tears into her eyes. The floating pollen seemed to be his notes made visible, and the dampness of the garden the weeping of the garden's sensibility. Though near nightfall, the rank-smelling weed-flowers glowed as if they would not close for intentness, and the waves of colour mixed with the waves of sound.

30 The light which still shone was derived mainly from a large hole in the western bank of cloud; it was like a piece of day left behind by accident, dusk having closed in elsewhere. He concluded his plaintive melody, a very simple performance, demanding no great skill; and she waited, thinking another might be begun. But, tired of playing, he had desultorily come round the fence, and was rambling up behind her. Tess, her
35 cheeks on fire, moved away furtively, as if hardly moving at all.

Discuss the means by which Hardy gives significance to the presence of Tess in the natural world in this extract **and** elsewhere in *Tess of the d'Urbervilles*.

33. Hogg

Analyse Hogg's uses of ambiguity of plot and character in *The Private Memoirs and Confessions of a Justified Sinner.*

34. Joyce

In the original exam paper, an extract comprising the first 3 or 4 pages of the opening chapter of A Portrait of the Artist as a Young Man *was supplied. However, due to copyright reasons we are unable to reproduce this text in our publication. We would therefore advise you to use a copy of the book alongside the following questions.*

Questions

(*a*) Analyse Joyce's use of narrative voice in this extract.

(*b*) Go on to discuss his use of narrative voice **either** elsewhere in *A Portrait of the Artist as a Young Man* or in any **two** of the short stories from *Dubliners*.

(Extract deleted for copyright reasons)

[Turn over

(Extract deleted for copyright reasons)

Questions

(*a*) Analyse Joyce's use of narrative voice in this extract.

(*b*) Go on to discuss his use of narrative voice **either** elsewhere in *A Portrait of the Artist as a Young Man* **or** in any **two** of the short stories from *Dubliners*.

35. Spark

Discuss the importance of setting—in both time and place—in *The Prime of Miss Jean Brodie* **and** in *The Girls of Slender Means*.

36. Stevenson

"*His art was to present moral argument in the form of entertainment.*"

Discuss *The Strange Case of Dr Jekyll and Mr Hyde* **and** *Weir of Hermiston* in the light of this assertion.

PROSE NON-FICTION

37. Autobiography

How effectively does any **one** of the specified authors exploit the form of the autobiography to comment on political, social or moral issues?

38. Autobiography

Compare and contrast **two** of the specified authors' treatments of aspects of their education, both formal and informal.

39. Travel Writing

To what extent can any **two** of the specified texts be said to present us with journeys of self-discovery?

40. Travel Writing

"*The first condition of right thought is right sensation—the first condition of understanding a foreign country is to smell it.*"

(T. S. Eliot)

How effectively does any **one** of the specified authors enable us to "*smell*" the country or countries that he visits?

41. Writing about Scotland

Describe some of the ways by which aspects of Scottish identity are defined in **one** or **more than one** of the specified texts.

42. Writing about Scotland

How effectively do any **two** of the specified texts convey to you the customs, the manners, the ways of life of Scotland—or of a particular part of Scotland—in past times?

[Turn over

Section 2—Language Study

You must answer **one question only** in this section.

Topic A—The use of English in a particular geographical area

1. Describe some of the ways speakers make use of **one** particular regional variety of English in different contexts.

2. Describe and account for some of the distinctive features of an overseas variety of English such as American, Jamaican or Indian.

Topic B—Variations in the use of English related to social class

As a starting point for both questions on this topic you are provided with a quotation. Read it carefully and then answer **either** question 3 **or** question 4.

"*If we look at things from a completely linguistic point of view, all the theorizing of the past sixteen years appears to have reduced to evidence that, in situations more artificial and alien to them than to middle-class children, working-class children use a higher proportion of pronouns. Is this what it has been all about?*"

(Peter Trudgill)

3. How persuasive do **you** find the evidence that there **are** substantial variations in the use of English related to social class?

4. What issues do researchers in this area of variations in the use of English related to social class need to address and how should they address them?

Topic C—Variations in the use of English related to gender

5. What has research suggested about the ways men and women interrupt and "hold the floor" in conversation? How does this research relate to your own experience?

6. "*Recent research on gender and language suggests that stories told by women are significantly different from stories told by men.*"

   (Suzanne Eggins and Diane Slade)

   From your own reading in this area and from your own experience and research, explain how and why stories told by women in conversation tend to differ from those told by men.

Topic D—The linguistic characteristics of informal conversation

For both questions on this topic, you are provided with an extract from a transcript of an informal conversation between two young women (I and M) who are meeting to discuss a joint project.

Read both questions and the extract carefully and then answer **either** question 7 **or** question 8.

7. Which features of informal conversation are shown in the transcript below?

From your understanding of this transcript and from your knowledge of other transcripts, discuss what other features of informal conversation you could show and why you would choose to do so.

8. Using the transcript below and examples from your own reading and study, make a case for **or** against the value of the detailed analysis of informal conversation.

Transcription Key

The lines have been numbered individually. Written punctuation, such as full stops and commas, has been avoided. The following transcription conventions have been used:

A cross represents a pause of up to one second	+
Capital letters indicate emphatic stress	YES
Non-verbal features are in square brackets	[laughs]
Round brackets are the transcriber's best guess at an unclear utterance	(amongst)

1	I:	so how are things (amongst) your um +
2		your holiday how was your holiday
3	M:	oh it was really funny the holiday was like really really awesome
4	I:	right
5	M:	and then my first day back I was like kicking back + in my
6		desk just still really relaxed and I
7	I:	trying to get back into it [laughs]
8	M:	yeah and a girl from (my-) a woman from my section came up
9		and said oh [inhales] do you want to do this horrible speech that
10		I have to give in front of students for work day they had career
11		work day thing and the students have to come in to the building
12		and I said
13	I:	yeah
14	M:	yeah yeah sure I'll do it and she goes [surprised tone] really I
15		thought I'd have to go down on my knees and BEG and I was
16		going oh no it's cool and I'm sure it was because I was just you
17		know still in holiday mode 'cause I don't normally like
18		speaking in front of anyone [laughs] but
19	I:	yeah
20	M:	yeah I agreed (to) and it was fine
21	I:	so you might have um taken er a while
22	M:	so [laughs]

23	I:	longer t- to come to the decision (would you) [laughs]
24	M:	yeah oh yeah I would have gone no no go away
25		but yeah it was really good
26	I:	it was a good trip oh (okay)
27	M:	yeah but now back into it again
28	I:	yeah things are pretty full on here
29	M:	yeah I can imagine
30	I:	mm sort of working I just did my first submission + for the
31		minister

Topic E—The linguistic characteristics of political communication

9. It is often claimed that the art of political communication was transformed by the arrival of television. Discuss some of the different ways in which politicians engage a television audience in contexts such as:

- party political broadcasts
- news reports
- interviews
- debates.

10. The following text is an extract from a transcript of a speech given by Jim Wallace, MSP, the Leader of the Liberal Democrats in Scotland, and Deputy First Minister in the Scottish Executive. The speech was given to a conference in Glasgow in November, 2002. For convenience of reference, each separate utterance has been numbered.

Make a detailed analysis of the language of the speech and assess its effectiveness as a piece of political communication. You might consider the following issues:

- how the speaker attempts to excite the emotions of his audience
- how he characterises his political allies
- how he characterises his political rivals
- how he refers to "the nation"
- how he uses humour in his speech.

[1] Soon the people of Scotland will have the chance to elect their second Parliament. [2] One of the key challenges facing it will be improving our public services. [3] Since 1999, we've increased capacity in those services, making considerable investment in improving facilities and training staff. [4] Over the next four years expectations of the new Executive and Parliament to deliver will properly increase. [5] People will rightly expect to see the difference we claim to make.

[6] So I want an election campaign focussed on genuine debate, not personalities. [7] That is why our campaigning will be based around three pillars:

1. Our record of achievement;

2. Our radical agenda to improve the choices and opportunities available to individuals; and

3. Our positive approach.

[8] There is one problem though. [9] From previous experience I just think I might be asked the coalition question. [10] I don't want that to detract from the real issues that affect people's lives. [11] So, I want to take this opportunity to make clear where we stand, in the hope that the campaign proper can focus on issues, not tactics.

[12] Those who get excited about which party might go into government with another should remember one simple thing: it is the views of the people of Scotland that should come first. [13] It is their votes that should count when governments are formed. [14] It is the proportional electoral system that ensures MSPs representing a majority of the people take the final decisions in the Scottish Parliament.

[15] At the last election, we were asked whether we would go into coalition with Labour or the SNP. [16] Our reply was straightforward. [17] We said we'd talk first to the party with the largest number of seats. [18] Even then, we made clear that we would only form a coalition if we could agree a liberal Programme for Government.

[19] This time, our emphasis on the need for a liberal Programme of Government will remain. [20] This time, though, the electoral landscape is clearer.

[21] This time, we know the outcome of the 1999 election. [22] And we know the trend of opinion polls – though as ever, they carry a health warning. [23] A year before the 1999 election the SNP were polling around 48%. [24] In fact, they got less than 30% of the vote. [25] For the last six months they have been becalmed at around 28% in opinion polls. [26] We know that the SNP claim all sorts of weird and wonderful things with no basis in fact. [27] But even they would be hard pressed to explain how a 20 point fall in support is a springboard for victory.

[28] We shouldn't be surprised that they are languishing in the polls. [29] Anyone watching TV coverage of Parliament and there are some—could not fail to be struck by the SNP's repeated whine, whinge and moan.

[30] And even when they do come up with something, such as their recent fifty-four page document Talking Independence, what do we find?

- The word Independence is referred to 211 times.

- And any mention of teachers? No.

- Any mention of passengers? No.

- Any mention of patients? No.

- Any mention of nurses? No.

- But, for the record, any mention of Embassies? Two.

[31] That is why I cannot foresee the circumstances in which the SNP would be in the position to pick up the phone after the next election. [32] And it is not my job as your leader to talk up the non-existent chances of other parties. [33] My job is to maximise the number of Liberal Democrat votes and seats that our party gains next May.

[34] So we'll campaign on our record:

- Tuition fees: abolished in Scotland, still there in England.
- Personal care for the elderly: free in Scotland, undelivered in England.
- Teachers' pay: new pay and conditions in Scotland, the envy of teachers in England.

[35] Governing on their own in England, Labour has failed to do any of these things. [36] In Scotland, it is the Liberal Democrats who've made the difference.

Topic F—The linguistic characteristics of tabloid journalism

For **both** questions on this topic, you are provided on *Pages nineteen and twenty* with extracts from *The Sun* newspaper, Tuesday, 26 November, 2002.

Read both the questions and the extracts carefully and then answer **either** question 11 **or** question 12.

11. "***Sun*** *readers might not be able to write like a* ***Sun*** *journalist but in a real sense they know the discourse and its meaning in advance.*"

In the editorial and in the article, identify aspects of style and language which a reader would expect to be part of tabloid journalism. How far is the "view of the world" represented here typical of tabloid journalism?

12. "*Much of the text of tabloid journalism is technically speaking aesthetic. It contains patterns of discourse which are literary rather than colloquial and includes poetic features such as alliteration, parallel phrase structure, metaphor and puns.*"

Discuss the editorial and article in the light of the above statement.

THE SUN SAYS

Brit lit's a hit

WHEN screen siren Nicole Kidman decides to swap glamour for literature we should take notice.

And when she chooses to play a British writer, Virginia Woolf, we should take it as a compliment.

Kate Winslet and Dame Judi Dench recently did a wonderful job playing the late novelist Iris Murdoch in the movies.

And Gwyneth Paltrow is portraying Sylvia Plath—the sad, complex American author who married English poet Ted Hughes.

What does all this mean?

It means English literature is box office.

The moneymen funding these movies are not running charities.

These are not "art house" films seen only by a few.

Hollywood has realised that films about incredible people make incredible viewing.

Mind you, don't expect a happy ending in any of these three films.

Iris Murdoch died after suffering from Alzheimer's.

The other two killed themselves...

[Turn over

THE RISE OF LATEST CINEMA BOOKBUSTERS

Why Hollywood's babes are queuing up to play literary giants in cardies

MENTION Nicole Kidman or Kate Winslet and you think of glamour-packed Hollywood blockbusters.

But the sexy stars are swapping the corsets they wore in Moulin Rouge and Titanic for cardigans and tweed skirts — to play dowdy English writers.

Screen beauties like Nicole, Kate, Gwyneth Paltrow and Julianne Moore are queuing up to make LitChick Flicks — the latest movie trend.

Ticket sales are suddenly less important than artistic merit, with a string of low-budget films about authors.

Filmgoers may not know much about the worthy poets and novelists — two of whom killed themselves — but many had wild and raunchy lives ideal for movie storylines.

The most amazing style change was Nicole Kidman's leap from a diamond-clad prostitute in Moulin Rouge to plain Virginia Woolf in The Hours.

Tortured

Bisexual English writer Woolf was a tortured genius who drowned herself in a river near her Sussex home in 1941.

Aussie actress Nicole, 35, was completely transformed for the part — donning a fake nose, a dark knotted wig and ill-fitting floral dress.

The trend was started by Britain's own Kate Winslet in Iris. She dressed in drab skirts and a bobbed blonde wig last year to play novelist Iris Murdoch, who died in 1999 from Alzheimer's.

The film — with Dame Judi Dench as the older Murdoch — won critical acclaim from both sides of the Atlantic.

Soon, more LitChick Flicks in the pipeline. Gwyneth Paltrow is to play tragic American poet Sylvia Plath in a £7 million British film on her tempestuous life with English poet laureate Ted Hughes.

Ted and Sylvia, now being shot in the UK by BBC films, charts their torrid love affair which lasted until Plath's suicide in 1963 at the age of 30. Meanwhile, Julianne Moore is lined up to play manic depressive poet Deirdre Burroughs in Running With Scissors. Filming starts next year.

So why has Hollywood fallen for female writers?

Nick James, editor of British film industry mag Sight & Sound, believes the movies are designed to bring older women back to cinemas. He says: "The industry is after women who gave up going to see films when blockbusters like Bond and Harry Potter took over."

Movie-makers have lost their female audience because the romantic comedies they like have died out, he adds.

He says: "This genre has more or less collapsed and the film industry hopes to revive interest through these biopics."

Nick also reckons the stars aim to boost their reputations — and gain award nominations.

BAFTA member Barry John, a retired film editor, agrees. He says Iris was praised by critics and got three Oscar nominations, winning one.

He adds: "It was also a story about scandal, as are the two new films about Virginia Woolf and Sylvia Plath.

"Scandal works very well on screen. Because these women were trailblazers, their lives were often excessive and off the moral scale of their age.

"It all makes for compelling viewing."

By KATY WEITZ

Topic G—The use of Scots in a particular geographical area

13. "*There can be no doubt that pure dialect speech is rapidly disappearing even in country districts, owing to the spread of education, and to modern facilities of intercommunication.*"

(Joseph Wright, 1898)

Drawing evidence from your study of the current use of Scots in a particular geographical area, discuss how far Wright's assertion can be said to be valid today.

14. Briefly describe the history and development of the Scots language of a particular geographical area. Consider whether its contemporary use has become restricted to particular situations and areas of experience.

Topic H—The linguistic characteristics of Scots as used in informal conversation

15. "*Many speakers continue to use Scots words, phrases and idioms everyday—and in doing so they are affirming the richness and usefulness of the modern Scottish tongue.*"

Drawing evidence from your research into the linguistic characteristics of Scots as used in informal conversation, comment on "*the richness and usefulness of the modern Scottish tongue*".

16. In the following extract, *CONVERSATION BETWEEN CAROL ANN, NAN AND DI*, identify the features of Nan's narrative which are typical of spoken language. Comment in detail on the ways she uses Scots language to engage her audience.

Conversation between Carol Ann, Nan and Di

Square brackets around words or dots [...] denote a section which is inaudible or which could not be transcribed with confidence. Sounds that are very lightly articulated or not articulated are marked by round brackets ( ) where this makes the transcription easier to follow.

CA: So you used to go to Rothesay for your [holidays]?

Nan: Oh we loved it, ay. She'll remember aw that daen't ye? She ... we used to go wi Ma and Archie. An it was a room an kitchen, an ma Ma was in this room wi the weans an A was in this bed recess an this ... Oh mind! One time A got sunburnt. We went tae that [whit dae ye ...] Kilchattan Bay.

Di: How d'ye get sunburnt at Ro(th)esay?

Nan A did. A got roastit.

Di In the photographs everybody's got their coats on [...]

Nan: Ah, but A ... A'd a bikini on. A bought this bikini right. It wis a royal blue an white stripe and A thought A wis the cat's whiskers. An A'm lyin at ... that wis when you didnae use ... [I mean] you couldn't afford the oil. Nobody ever mentioned the oil or any cream or anyhin for yer legs. Huh! Nae wonder they're aw wrinkles the day. An a wis lyin at Kilchatten Bay an the weans are aw playin aboot. That wis aw right [ye just got up] "That's us. We'll aw go home." See that night! My knees wouldnae bend. Ma legs were absolutely roasted. A couldnae get intae bed. A'd tae sit wi ma legs hingin oot the bed, d'you remember? No you'll no remember, you were only a wee lassie.

Di: [I don't remember ...]

Nan: [Goin like that ... do remember.] Ma legs! Oh A wis only a [wee] young lassie at the time. But Oh did A suffer. Let me tell ... That wis just nae oil. A've never ... A don't think A've ever sunbathed since. A wis absolutely that colour. Ma legs an ma belly right across (th)ere. An A thought A wis gonnae look like a film star [...]

Christine Robinson and Carol Ann Crawford (2001) "Scotspeak" Perth: SLRC
ISBN 1 899920013 (page 44)

Topic I—Variations in the use of Scots among older and younger people

17. Account for variations in the use of Scots among older and younger people.

18. "*Young people constantly rework the language of their elders to make it relevant to their own experience.*"

What evidence have you found of this process in your study of the use of Scots among older and younger people?

Topic J—Uses of Scots in the media

19. How convincing in form and content is the use of Scots language in film and television?

You should support your answer with detailed reference to **one** or **more than one** text you have studied.

20. Describe in detail how print journalism **or** broadcasting **or** advertising has been enlivened and enriched by the use of Scots language.

Topic K—Uses of Scots in contemporary literature

21. Describe and analyse the use of **two** or **more than two** varieties of Scots in contemporary literature.

22. For this question, you are provided (*Page twenty-three*) with two texts in each of which aspects of Shakespeare's tragedy *Hamlet* are adapted and commented on in Scots.

Compare and contrast the principal linguistic features of the Scots used in each of the texts.

OOR HAMLET

There was this king sleeping in his gairden a'alane
When his brither in his ear drapped a wee tait o'henbane.
Then he stole his brither's crown and his money and his widow
But the deid king walked and goat his son and said, "Hey, listen kiddo!"
5 "Ah've been killt and it's your duty to take revenge oan Claudius.
Kill him quick and clean and show the nation whit a fraud he is"
The boay says, "Right, Ah'll dae it, but Ah'll huvti play it crafty.
So that naeb'dy will suspect me, Ah'll kid oan that Ah'm a daftie."

So wi' a' except Horatio (and he trusts him as a friend),
10 Hamlet - that's the boay - kids oan he's roon the bend,
And because he wisnae ready for obligatory killing
He tried to make the king think he was tuppence aff the shilling;
Took the mickey oot Polonius, treatit poor Ophelia vile,
And tellt Rosencrantz and Guildenstern that Denmark was a jile.
15 Then a troupe o' travelling actors, like 7.84
Arrived to dae a special wan-night gig in Elsinore.

Hamlet, Hamlet! Loved his mammy.
Hamlet, Hamlet! Acting balmy.
Hamlet, Hamlet! Hesitating.
20 Wonders if the ghost's a cheat and that is why he's waiting.

(Adam McNaughton)

WI A NAUKIT DIRKIE

D'ye mind hou Hamlet wad aye girn an chirk
wi aw yon speik: *tae be or no tae be*
an et the enn o't aa he cudna see
his wey tae jag his belly wi a dirk?
5 Yon Mouss-trap geggie, yon wes sleekit wark
tae shaw hou pushent lug-holes gar ye dee;
an aa yon Freudian Psychologie
tae frichten Gertrude oot o her nicht-sark.

An auu fur whit? "Wes Hamlet gyte? Discuss." . . .
10 Still naebodie seems tae ken for aa the scrievin.
As the Bard says himsel: *the rest is silence.*

Yon "kintra maitters" cam tae sic a pass:
droont sweethairts, arras-proggin, audience-deavin:
aa juist a ploy tae gie's mair sex and violence.

(William Neill)

Topic L—Uses of Scots in specialised fields

23. Discuss in detail the linguistic features of the Scots used in any specialised field you have studied.

24. Compare and contrast the ways in which the resources of Scots have been deployed in **two** specialised fields you have studied.

Section 3—Textual Analysis

You must answer **one question only** in this section.

1. **Prose fiction [*Pages twenty-four to twenty-six*]**

In this question you are presented with two extracts from the early pages of novels.

Extract A is from ***Gentlemen in England*** *(1985) by AN Wilson.*
Extract B is from ***The Story of Lucy Gault*** *(2002) by William Trevor.*

In each extract the writer is presenting a setting:

- *in Extract A, the Bower, Abbey Grove, the home of the Nettleship family*
- *in Extract B, Lahardane, the home of Captain Everard Gault and his family.*

Read both extracts carefully and then answer the question that follows them (Page twenty-six).

EXTRACT A

The sun had been doing its best, since dawn, to shed a little light into The Bower, Abbey Grove, but it was on the point of recognising its match in the Nettleships and going behind a thick black cloud. Earlier, from a bright cyaneous firmament, it had smiled down on St John's Wood, but it found difficulty, when it came to The Bower, in
5 getting past the high hedges, the tall fir trees in the garden, and the laurels in the shrubbery before it got to the house. Still, the sun had done it, and made a manly show of falling upon the garish mullioned Gothic, some thirty years old, where the professor and his household chose to reside, an asymmetrical, unhappy-looking house which sprouted turrets and porches and balconies where you least expected them. Lest the
10 sunlight thought to pierce the windows or balconies, the wary Nettleships had erected a good deal of ironwork (Fish and Co) in the way of railings, balustrades, drainpipes and lattices and then, as though faintly ashamed of the architectural exuberance of the exterior, they had trained an abundant Virginia creeper to swamp its walls from the area to the highest tower. The combination of red brick excrescences and the green of
15 the creeper suggested that a giant piece of meat had been cast down in the garden, a raw leg of mutton perhaps, hastily covered with a liberal coating of mint sauce to disguise the fact that it had not been properly cooked.

Human entrants, no less than the sun, might find The Bower forbidding, or at any event be struck by how fiercely it hid itself from itself, how generously it was swathed.
20 The front door itself was thickly draped with a heavy curtain, the weight and texture of a carpet, and intruders were admitted by a maid who existed beneath several layers of linen and starched muslin. In all probability there was a staircase beneath the thick carpets and the brass rods over which you would tread, just as to your right, behind a clutter of vulgar prints by Spy and the ornately floral wallpaper, there might arguably
25 have been a wall.

Whether there were any walls left in the drawing room into which you would now be admitted is an altogether more dubious consideration, for, on all sides, there was not only a more generously entwined floral pattern—michaelmas daisies rampaging from dark brown wainscotting to fudgy ceiling, but almost every one of the little purple
30 blooms was itself obscured by a heavy frame of gilt or walnut. There were four enormous canvases representing Scotch animals in varying degrees of decomposition.

Some shaggy Highland cattle—themselves as well-swathed as The Bower—gazed, in one painting, across the room towards a stag being torn apart by hounds, Blair Atholl or Glen Somewhair or Castle Mack—something glimpsed in the background.
35 Between these disconcerting reminders of "nature red in tooth and claw" there were an abundance of portraits in oval frames, persons redder in cheek than in claw whom it would have been safe to conclude to be Nettleships. And those oval-framed, ill-favoured cousins, uncles, grandsires and aunts of the professor fought for space among the michaelmas daisies with views of Vesuvius, Etna, and other famous volcanoes of
40 the world. Somewhere in the middle of it all there was a representation of Her Majesty the Queen.

Not much of this was seen by daylight. It needed the gas, as the professor said, to be seen at its best. Mere morning sunbeams could not get at it, through the creeper and the ironwork, or within the half-closed Nottingham lace curtains, and the further
45 lined draperies of heavy green velvet which festooned the dark brown of the Gothic window frames. Such sunbeams as penetrated the swooping lace and velvet fell into a chaos of immovables and seemed to hop about as if they knew they were there under sufferance and only dared to light up one object in three. Here, as in the hallway, everything was adorned or draped or covered. The stained oak boards of the floor
50 groaned beneath the suffocating carpet, itself darkly invisible under the sofas, chairs, occasional tables, bureaus and bookcases. Tables, chiefly octagonal in shape, were concealed with an undercloth of baize or velvet and an overcloth of cream-coloured Nottingham lace to match the curtains. A similar drapery protected the marble chimney-piece, on whose lacy and multi-levelled surfaces, as on all available table tops,
55 there rioted an abundance of clutter, Staffordshire shepherds and shepherdesses: a bronze Laocöon, wrestling with snakes, or perhaps merely tearing at the snakes in exasperation at the sight of so many Nettleships; fans; snuff boxes, pin boxes, card boxes, a plenitude of every imaginable kind of box in gaily-coloured woods and mother of pearl. On the writing desk, as too on the chimney-piece, dozens of Nettleships, ages
60 and genders various, closed photographic ranks and peered at the cows and the statuary from knobbly silver frames. On the wall opposite the windows, a walnut piano sprouted brass candlesticks.

In the middle of all this, Maudie sat with her mother and embroidered cream jug covers for a silent space.

EXTRACT B

There was no other place he might more happily have lived than beneath the slated roof of its three grey storeys, the stone softened by the white woodwork of the windows and the delicate fanlight above a white hall door. Flanking it on its right was the wide high archway of a cobbled yard, with cobbled passageways leading to an apple
5 orchard and a garden. One half of the circle on to which the front rooms looked out was the gravel sweep; the other was a raised lawn that was separated from steeply rising woods by a curve of blue hydrangeas. The upstairs rooms at the back had a view of the sea as far as the sea's horizon.

The origins of the Gaults in Ireland had centuries ago misted over. Previously of
10 Norfolk—so it was believed within the family, although without much certainty—they had settled first of all in the far western reaches of County Cork. A soldier of fortune had established their modest dynasty, lying low there for reasons that were not known. Some time in the early eighteenth century the family had moved east, respectable and well-to-do by then, one son or another of each generation continuing

15 the family's army connection. The land at Lahardane was purchased; the building of the house began. The long, straight avenue was made, lines of chestnut trees planted along it on either side, the woodlands of the glen laid out. Later generations planted the orchard, with stock from County Armagh; the garden, kept small, was created bit by bit. In 1769 Lord Townshend, the Lord Lieutenant, stayed at Lahardane; in 1809
20 Daniel O'Connell did when there wasn't a bedroom unoccupied at the Stuarts' Dromana. History touched the place in that way; but as well-remembered, as often talked about, were births and marriages and deaths, domestic incidents, changes and additions to this room or that, occasions of anger or reconciliation. Suffering a stroke, a Gault in 1847 lay afflicted for three years yet not insensible. There was a disastrous
25 six months of card-playing in 1872 during which field after field was lost to the neighbouring O'Reillys. There was the diphtheria outbreak that spread so rapidly and so tragically in 1901, sparing only the present Everard Gault and his brother in a family of five. Above the writing-desk in the drawing-room there was a portrait of a distant ancestor whose identity had been unknown for as long as anyone of the present
30 could remember: a spare, solemn countenance where it was not whiskered, blue unemphatic eyes. It was the only portrait in the house, although since photography had begun there were albums that included the images of relatives and friends as well as those of the Gaults of Lahardane.

All this—the house and the remnants of the pasture land, the seashore below the
35 pale clay cliffs, the walk along it to the fishing village of Kilauran, the avenue over which the high branches of the chestnut trees now met—was as much part of Everard Gault as the features of his face were, the family traits that quite resembled a few of those in the drawing-room portrait, the smooth dark hair. Tall and straight-backed, a man who hid nothing of himself, slight in his ambitions now, he had long ago accepted
40 that his destiny was to keep in good heart what had been his inheritance, to attract bees to his hives, to root up his failing apple trees and replace them. He swept the chimneys of his house himself, could repoint its mortar and replace its window glass. Creeping about on its roof, he repaired in the lead the small perforations that occurred from time to time, the Seccotine he squeezed into them effective for a while.

Question

Show how each writer uses aspects of setting to establish character. In your answer you should pay particular attention to similarities and differences in approach.

2. Prose non-fiction [*Pages twenty-seven to thirty*]

The following piece of writing ***Among Chickens*** *by Jonathan Miller was published in 1988.*

Read it carefully and then answer questions (a) and (b) that follow it (Page thirty).

1

I never had a sense of humour. What started me in a theatrical direction was finding at a very early age that I had a talent. In fact, not so much a talent as a disability: I could impersonate chickens. I *was* a chicken. I said to people, "I will imitate a chicken for you," and this pleased them. I don't know why. It did. 5 Therefore I became extremely observant of the minute dialect of chickens.

For example, I became very interested in this double thing they have: it starts off with "*buk, buk, buk, buk*", and then "*bacagh*" follows. I noticed that some of the cruder impersonators of chickens, and there were competitors at school, never understood that there was a rather subtle variation of "*buk, buk, buk*" for every "*bacagh*". They 10 used to think it was absolutely regular. But I noticed, and this was really a big breakthrough in chicken linguistics, that chickens liked to lead you up the garden path. They would lead you to expect that for every four or five "*buk*" there would be a "*bacagh*"; so people, the bad chicken impersonators, the unobservant ones, would go as follows: "*Buk, buk, buk, buk, bacagh, buk, buk, buk, buk, bacagh, buk, buk, buk, buk, buk,* 15 *bacagh.*" What I noticed, after prolonged examination, was an entirely different pattern of chicken speech behaviour. Thus: "*Buk, buk, buk, buk, buk, buk, bacagh, buk, buk, bacagh, buk, buk, buk, buk, buk, buk, buk, buk . . . BACAGH, buk, buk. . .*"

I conducted this examination during the war, when food was short and we used to get food parcels from the United States, which for some reason always took the form of 20 cling peaches. I don't know what the Americans thought we were suffering from— massive cling peach deficiency presumably. And one of the ways my own family was digging for victory was to rear chickens. We moved around a lot, following my father from one military hospital to another, not because he was a patient, but because he was a military psychiatrist. Everywhere we went, we took a trailer behind the car, filled 25 with hens. They would be kept in a camp at the bottom of the garden, like displaced persons. I watched these creatures for hours on end. They tormented me.

2

I offer an example of humour from my professional experience. Recently, I directed a production of Eugene O'Neill's *Long Day's Journey Into Night*. I wanted to see what would happen if I treated the play not as a Greek tragedy, which is what 30 O'Neill wanted, but as an orphan object that I had just found. And it struck me, as a foreigner, that it was a highly skilful version of a family squabble. Therefore, it seemed to me, it was necessary to get away from the usual incantatory manner of performing O'Neill and restore to the play the quality of conversation. In the process of making it like conversation something happened: it produced laughter. It was like moving a 35 match over the abrasive surface on the box. If you move the match slowly, nothing happens, but if you strike at the right tempo—flames. There is the moment at the end of the play, when the mother comes downstairs in a demented state of morphine intoxication and the drunken elder brother turns and says, "The mad scene, enter Ophelia." The scene developed a momentum as we rehearsed, increasing in pace until 40 the first preview the actor playing the part rose to his feet and said, at *terrific* speed, "The mad scene, enter Ophelia," and there was a roar of laughter from the audience. We had struck the match. The actor, afterwards, was devastated.

It was much earlier, in fact—while Peter Cook, Alan Bennett, Dudley Moore and myself were performing "Beyond the Fringe"—that I became very interested in what 45 was happening up there on the stage, what it was that produced this strange respiratory convulsion. By the thousandth performance, it sounds like a sudden explosion, a noise from another planet. I became fascinated with laughter.

I had trained as a biologist and felt that if we do something from which we get acute pleasure, like laughter, it must have been planted in us, or else we acquired it, because 50 it has powerful selective advantage. We wouldn't, that is, have the *experience* of pleasure unless there was, for the species, some sort of selective advantage in the *behaviour* that leads to it. Which immediately raises the question: what is it that nature gets out of the pleasure we take from laughter? There are various theories. Henri Bergson thought it was the collective criticism of some anomalous and unfruitful 55 behaviour on the part of one member of the herd. Freud saw it as the release of tension following the sudden introduction of forbidden material into consciousness.

I prefer to think something much more comprehensive is going on when we get pleasure out of, say, hearing a joke. Jokes are of course peculiar and rather limited examples, a subset of the large domain of humour. I think that jokes are a social 60 lubricant—sometimes a highly formulaic one—that we use for the purposes of maintaining conviviality, especially among men. Men, as soon as they are in all-male company, start telling jokes like it was some sort of convulsion. In fact, one of the more trying features of being with lots of men is that jokes break out like an illness. It's a way of both keeping one's distance and registering membership of a group when 65 there are no spontaneous grounds for shared membership. So-and-so says, "Have you heard the one about bum bum bum bum?" and someone else says, "That reminds me, did you hear the one about bum bum bum bum?" and before you know where you are there's a competitive fugue of joke-telling, like the Kwakiutl Indians who throw piles of blankets and copper shields into the sea in a demonstration of competitive 70 hospitality. Jokes are a sign that you have in your pocket a social currency that allows you to join the game.

I'm fascinated by the ritual procedure of the exchange and also the obligatory response. In only one joke out of five is that response spontaneous laughter. The rest of the time the joke-hearers feel it incumbent on themselves to contribute a skilful 75 impersonation of being killed with laughter. You hold your sides, you slap your thighs, you say, "Doggone." And this is simply to maintain that joke-teller's self-esteem. It is almost impossible, unless you are insensitive or almost pathologically sadistic, to withhold the impersonation of laughter from someone who has just told you a joke.

In fact, jokes have little to do with spontaneous humour. The teller has the same 80 relationship to them that he or she might have to a Hertz Rent-a-Car. A joke is a hired object, with many previous users, and very often its ashtrays are filled with other people's cigarettes, and its gears are worn and slipping, because other people have driven this joke very badly before you got behind the wheel.

Jokes also conform to strict patterns, one of the most common being any one of a 85 number of jocular trinities that cruise the world: "There was this English fellow, an Irishman and a Jewish fellow." They have a toy mechanism which is very simple and very conventional. It would not be difficult, I suspect, to produce a taxonomy of *all* jokes. There are not many types. There is the type about the deaf, blind or disabled; the type involving different nationalities; and the type that, while still formulaic, draws 90 on the news. For example: the *Challenger* jokes after the Shuttle disaster, the Chicken Kiev jokes after Chernobyl.

And when you laugh at any one of these various types you're really laughing at the predictable, or rather at the strange tension that exists between predictable generalization and a specific instance of it. Take the Jack Benny joke which was on one 95 of his radio shows. We hear footsteps coming up behind Jack Benny, and a voice saying, "Your money or your life." There's silence. The voice repeats, "Your money or your life." And there's another long gap before Benny says, "I'm thinking." This is a pretty good joke; it relies on a generalization familiar to the audience—Jack Benny is very mean—and it works because it is a surprising way of reacquainting the audience 100 with the generalization. When you laugh, you're laughing at the very specific way Jack Benny has characterized himself.

I remember a sketch in "Beyond the Fringe". Peter Cook was a strange, rather withdrawn man in a shabby raincoat, sitting on a bench blankly asserting that he could have been a judge only he didn't have the Latin for the judging exams. He said, 105 "They're extremely rigorous, the judging exams, as compared to the mining exams which are extremely unrigorous, see. They only ask you one question: 'What is your name?' I got seventy-five per cent on that."

For years I tried to work out precisely why this was funny. On one level it's obvious, but there is more to it than simply the obvious. It is an instance of what a 110 philosopher would call a category mistake: it is in the nature of names that they are not something you can have seventy-five per cent knowledge of. You either know them or you don't. The sketch makes us conscious of something we know but don't generally think about, because it occurs at a pre-attentive level. You can only be examined on subjects in which there can be a scale of success. And knowing one's name is not, 115 actually, one of those things.

3

My mother was quite a bit different from my father. She was a writer, and had published her first novel when she was nineteen. She wrote all day and every day, and was rather intolerant of the noise made by her small children. She didn't like intrusions. She battered away on this funny little typewriter. She used the same one 120 until she died. That was what she was like. She preserved in her life a scrupulous monotony. She rose at the same time every day, sent us to school and began to tap away at the typewriter, or else noted sentences, or fragments of sentences, on the slit-open envelopes of letters she'd received that morning, a habit encouraged by the paper shortage during the war. She would put away her typewriter at twelve-thirty prompt 125 when we came back for lunch. This would be a rather glum meal of boiled chicken, not one of the chickens we kept, but another chicken, a chicken which looked as though it had never said a single "*bacagh*" in its entire life and had been simply tipped into hot water and come out with that awful goose-pimpled appearance that boiled chickens have. We ate the same meal every day. Boiled chicken, year in, year out.

130 My mother was an admirer of a little-known French writer whose name was Francis Ponge, a sort of parody name. Ponge was a man after my mother's own heart. Ponge wrote in minute detail about the appearance of such things as sand and mimosa and soap. Soap particularly fascinated him. Ponge wrote long essays on the appearance of soap, page after page of descriptions of soap. He wrote a novel titled *Soap*. My 135 mother translated some of his poetry. This also concerned soap.

[Turn over

My mother taught me something of which I was very impatient at the time: the value of monotony. With hindsight I see that the imposition of her routine was in effect a spiritual exercise which has lasted the rest of my life. She saw epiphanies in the mundane.

140 Eventually I became fascinated by the appearance of the commonplace as well. I learned the pleasure of simply watching. I take enormous pleasure from watching, in restaurants, in railway carriages or on street-corners. Anywhere. Elevators are good places. I like to see the way we handle social encounters at awkward moments. I like to see the little signs, the tiny gestures, the twitches and grimaces of embarrassment. And
145 it is here, amid the most minute detail of the commonplace and the ordinary and the mundane, that I find the greatest displays of humour.

4

Finally, I also like to remember the noise of certain English steam trains. English steam trains which used to make a noise as they pulled out of smoky, bronchitic stations in North London. Hmmm. This is very long ago. I see myself in short
150 trousers thinking about Betty Grable. First of all it was the whistle of the trains. "*Whooooooooo.*" Then: "*Chkuu, chkuu, ching, chkuu, chkuu, ching, chkuu, ching, chkuu, ching, chkuu, ching, chkuu, chkuu, ching, chkuu, chkuu* (faster and faster, softening to a gentle rhythm), *chkuu, ching, ching, chkuu, chkuu, ching, chkuu, ching, chkuu, chkuu, ching, ching, chkuu, chkuu, ching.*"

155 And so forth.

Questions

(*a*) Analyse the techniques used by Miller in his exploration of various aspects of humour.

(*b*) Do you consider the passage to be an effective piece of writing?

You should support your answer to this question with detailed comment on:

- structure
- tone
- any other features you consider to be important.

3. Poetry [*Page thirty-one*]

Read carefully the poem ***Indian Summer*** *(1996) by Tracey Herd and then answer the question that follows it.*

INDIAN SUMMER

That summer was hotter than any other
in my life-time. My bare knees
itched and burned in the sand
as I dug and dug for the rusted coins
5 that Nanny had hidden that morning.
I'd watched her from my bedroom window.

The rugs hung heavy on the line
with a row of scalps put there to dry—
my whole family wiped out by Indians,
10 shock woven brightly into their faces.

The sky burned blue as a flame.
Grass browned. I could have rubbed
two stones together and the flare
would have shot me like a rocket
15 into the wilderness.

I exchanged the coins for a pony
the colour of gun-metal
and hoisted myself up into the saddle,
wincing as my half-peeled thighs
20 stuck to the hot leather,
and punctured his flanks with my spurs.
He hollered, balancing on his shaggy hind legs
before hitting the dirt at a gallop.

He stretched out over the blazing pampas
25 leaving my mother lying awkwardly
in the gaudily striped deck-chair,
blood dripping delicately
down the cut stem of her neck.

Question

By what means—and how effectively—does the poet give significance to "That summer . . ."?

In answering this question, you may wish to consider the importance of:

- mood and atmosphere
- aspects of structure
- sound
- word choice
- imagery.

4. Drama [*Pages thirty-two to thirty-seven*]

In Brian Friel's play ***Philadelphia Here I Come*** *(1964), the main character is Gareth O'Donnell, known as Gar. Gar's father, S.B. O'Donnell, keeps a general store in the small Irish town, Ballybeg, where, as a county councillor, he has some status in the community. Gar has lived in Ballybeg with his father all his life, but is now preparing to emigrate to the USA.*

Throughout the play Gar is represented on stage by two actors. One actor plays Public, representing the outer, public face and voice of Gar; the other plays Private, the man within, the conscience, Gar's secret self. Nobody on stage, except Public, can hear Private when he speaks, and even Public never sees him and never looks at him.

The extract that follows is from the closing scene of the play. The action takes place in the kitchen of their home which is linked to the shop by a door, stage left. It is the early hours of the morning on which Gar is due to leave.

The characters in the extract are:

PUBLIC	*the outer Gar O'Donnell*
PRIVATE	*the hidden, inner Gar O'Donnell*
S.B.	*S.B. O'Donnell, Gar's father*
MADGE	*their elderly servant.*

Read the extract carefully and then answer the question that follows it (Page thirty-seven).

[*The small hours of the morning. The kitchen is dimly lit. In the kitchen, just outside the bedroom door, are Gar's cases, and lying across them are his coat, his cap, and a large envelope containing his X-ray and visa. The bedroom is in darkness: just enough light to see* PUBLIC *on the bed and* PRIVATE *in the chair.* S.B. *comes in from the scullery carrying a cup*
5 *of tea in his hand. He is dressed in long trousers, a vest, a hat, socks. He moves slowly towards the table, sees the cases, goes over to them, touches the coat, goes back towards the table, and sits there, staring at the bedroom door. He coughs.*

Immediately PRIVATE *is awake and* PUBLIC *sits up sleepily in bed.*]

PRIVATE: What—what—what's that? [*Relaxing.*] Madge probably. Looking
10 to see is the door bolted.
[PUBLIC *gets out of bed and switches on the light. Looks at his watch.*]
You'll not sleep again tonight, laddo.

PUBLIC: Blast!
[PUBLIC *looks at himself in the mirror and then sits on edge of bed.*]

15 PRIVATE: Four more hours. This is the last time you'll lie in this bed, the last time you'll look at that pattern on the wallpaper, the last time you'll listen to the silence of Ballybeg, the last time you'll—

PUBLIC: Agh, shut up!

PRIVATE: Go into the shop, man, and get yourself a packet of aspirin; that'll do
20 the trick. [*Looking up at ceiling.*] Mind if I take a packet of aspirin, Screwballs? Send the bill to the USA, okay? Out you go, boy, and get a clatter of pills!
[*They both go into the kitchen.* PUBLIC *stops dead when he sees* S.B. *staring at him.*]

25 PUBLIC: My God! Lady Godiva!

PRIVATE: Is this where you are?

S.B.: Aye — I — I — I — I wasn't sleeping. What has you up?
[PUBLIC *goes to where the key of the shop is hung up.*]

PUBLIC: I — I wasn't sleeping either. I'll get some aspirins inside.

30 S.B.: It's hard to sleep sometimes . . .

PUBLIC: It is, aye . . . sometimes . . .

S.B.: There's tea in the pot.

PUBLIC: Aye?

S.B.: If it's a headache you have.

35 PUBLIC: It'll make me no worse anyway.
[PUBLIC *goes into the scullery.* PRIVATE *stands at the door and talks into him.*]

PRIVATE: Now's your time, boy. The small hours of the morning. Put your head on his shoulder and say, "How's my wee darling Daddy?"
40 [PUBLIC *puts his head round the door.*]

PUBLIC: You take some?

S.B.: Sure you know I never take a second cup.

PRIVATE: Playing hard to get. Come on, bucko; it's your place to make the move – the younger man. Say—say—say—say, 'Screwballs, with two
45 magnificent legs like that, how is it you were never in show biz?' Say —oh, my God—say—say something.
[PUBLIC *enters with a cup of tea.*]

PUBLIC: You'll need a new tyre for the van.

S.B.: What one's that?

50 PUBLIC: The back left-hand one. I told you. It's done.

S.B.: Aye. So you did.

PUBLIC: And — and —

PRIVATE: What else?

PUBLIC: — and don't forget the fencing posts for McGuire next Wednesday.

55 S.B.: Fencing posts.

PUBLIC: Twelve dozen. The milk lorry'll take them. I spoke to Packey.

S.B.: Aye . . . right . . .

PRIVATE: Go on! Keep talking!

	PUBLIC:	And if you're looking for the pliers, I threw them into the tea chest
60		under the counter.
	S.B.:	Which tea chest?
	PUBLIC:	The one near the window.
	S.B.:	Oh, I see—I see . . .
	PRIVATE:	You're doing grand. Keep at it. It's the silence that's the enemy.
65	PUBLIC:	You'll be wanting more plug tobacco. The traveller'll be here this week.
	S.B.:	More plug.
	PUBLIC:	It's finished. The last of it went up to Curran's wake.
	S.B.:	I'll—I'll see about that.
70	PUBLIC:	And you'll need to put a new clasp on the lower window—the tinkers are about again.
	S.B.:	Aye?
	PUBLIC:	They were in at dinner time. I got some cans off them.
	S.B.:	I just thought I noticed something shining from the ceiling.
75	PUBLIC:	It's the cans then.
	S.B.:	Aye.
	PUBLIC:	That's what it is. I bought six off them.
	S.B.:	They'll not go to loss.
	PUBLIC:	They wanted me to take a dozen but I said six would do us.
80	S.B.:	Six is plenty. They don't go as quick as they used to—them cans.
	PUBLIC:	They've all got cookers and ranges and things.
	S.B.:	What's that?
	PUBLIC:	I say they don't buy them now because the open fires are nearly all gone.
85	S.B.:	That's it. All cookers and ranges and things these times.
	PUBLIC:	That's why I wouldn't take the dozen.
	S.B.:	You were right, too. Although I mind the time when I got through a couple of dozen a week.
	PUBLIC:	Aye?
90	S.B.:	All cans it was then. Maybe you'd sell a kettle at turf-cutting or if there'd be a Yank coming home . . . [*Pause.*]
	PUBLIC:	Better get these pills and then try to get a couple of hours sleep—
	S.B.:	You're getting the mail-van to Strabane?
95		[PUBLIC *gives him a quick, watchful look.*]

	PUBLIC:	At a quarter past seven.
	S.B.:	[*Awkwardly.*] I was listening to the weather forecast there . . . moderate westerly winds and occasional showers it said.
	PUBLIC:	Aye?
100	S.B.:	I was thinking it—it—it—it would be a fair enough day for going up in thon plane.
	PUBLIC:	It should be, then.
	S.B.:	Showers—just like the Canon said . . . And I was meaning to tell you that you should sit at the back . . .
105	PRIVATE:	—the longest way round's the shortest way home—
	S.B.:	So *he* was saying, too . . . you know there—if there was an accident or anything—it's the front gets it hardes—
	PUBLIC:	I suppose that's true enough.
110	S.B.:	So *he* was saying . . . not that I would know—just that he was saying it there . . .
	PRIVATE:	[*Urgently, rapidly.*] Now! Now! He might remember—he might. But if he does, my God, laddo—what if he does?
	PUBLIC:	[*With pretended carelessness.*] D'you know what kept coming into my mind the day?
115	S.B.:	Eh?
	PUBLIC:	The fishing we used to do on Lough na Cloc Cor.
	S.B.:	[*Confused, on guard.*] Oh, aye, Lough na Cloc Cor—aye—aye—
	PUBLIC:	We had a throw on it every Sunday during the season.
	S.B.:	That's not the day nor yesterday.
120	PUBLIC:	[*More quickly.*] There used to be a blue boat on it—d'you remember it?
	S.B.:	Many's the fish we took off that same lake.
	PUBLIC:	D'you remember the blue boat?
	S.B.:	A blue one, eh?
125	PUBLIC:	I don't know who owned it. But it was blue. And the paint was peeling.
	S.B.:	[*Remembering.*] I mind a brown one the doctor brought from somewhere up in the—
130	PUBLIC:	[*Quickly.*] It doesn't matter who owned it. It doesn't even matter that it was blue. But d'you remember one afternoon in May—we were up there—the two of us—and it must have rained because you put your jacket round my shoulders and gave me your hat—
	S.B.:	Aye?
135	PUBLIC:	—and it wasn't that we were talking or anything—but suddenly—suddenly you sang "All Round My Hat I'll Wear a Green Coloured Ribbono"—

S.B.: Me?

PUBLIC: —for no reason at all except that we—that you were happy. D'you remember? D'you remember?

140 [*There is a pause while* S.B. *tries to recall.*]

S.B.: No . . . no, then, I don't . . .
[PRIVATE *claps his hands in nervous mockery.*]

PRIVATE: [*Quickly.*] There! There! There!

S.B.: "All Round My Hat"? No, I don't think I ever knew that one. It
145 wasn't "The Flower of Sweet Strabane", was it? That was my song.

PUBLIC: It could have been. It doesn't matter.

PRIVATE: So now you know: it never happened! Ha-ha-ha-ha-ha.

S.B.: "All Round My Hat"? —that was never one of mine. What does it go like?

150 PUBLIC: I couldn't tell you. I don't know it either.

PRIVATE: Ha-ha-ha-ha-ha-ha-ha-ha.

S.B.: And you say the boat was blue?

PUBLIC:: It doesn't matter. Forget it.

S.B.: [*Justly, reasonably.*] There was a brown one belonging to the doctor,
155 and before that there was a wee flat-bottom—but it was green—or was it white? I'll tell you, you wouldn't be thinking of a punt—it could have been blue—one that the curate had down at the pier last summer—
[PRIVATE'S *mocking laughter increases.* PUBLIC *rushes quickly into the*
160 *shop.* PRIVATE, *still mocking, follows.*]
—a fine sturdy wee punt it was, too, and it could well have been the . . .
[*He sees that he is alone and tails off. Slowly he gets to his feet and goes towards the scullery door. He meets* MADGE *entering. She is dressed in outside clothes. She is very weary.*]

165 MADGE: What has you up?

S.B.: Me? Aw, I took medicine and the cramps wouldn't let me sleep. I thought you were in bed?

MADGE: I was over at Nelly's. The place was upside down.

S.B.: There's nothing wrong, is there?

170 MADGE: Not a thing.

S.B.: The baby's strong and healthy?

MADGE: Grand—grand.

S.B.: That's all that matters.

MADGE: They're going to call it Brigid.

175 S.B.: Brigid—that's a grand name . . . Patrick, Brigid, and Colmcille . . .
[*She takes off her hat and coat.*]
Madge . . .

	MADGE:	You'll get a cold padding about in yon rig.
	S.B.:	Madge, I'll manage rightly, Madge, eh?
180	MADGE:	Surely you will.
	S.B.:	I'll get one of Charley Bonner's boys to do the van on Tuesdays and Thursdays and I'll manage rightly?
	MADGE:	This place is cold. Away off to bed.
	S.B.:	It's not like in the old days when the whole countryside did with me;
185		I needed the help then. But it's different now. I'll manage by myself now. Eh? I'll manage fine, eh?
	MADGE:	Fine.
	S.B.:	D'you mind the trouble we had keeping him at school just after he turned ten. D'you mind nothing would do him but he'd get behind
190		the counter. And he had this wee sailor suit on him this morning—
	MADGE:	A sailor suit? He never had a sailor suit.
	S.B.:	Oh, he had, Madge. Oh, Madge, he had. I can see him, with his shoulders back, and the wee head up straight, and the mouth, aw, man, as set, and says he this morning, I can hear him saying it, says
195		he, "I'm not going to school. I'm going into my daddy's business"—you know—all important—and, d'you mind, you tried to coax him to go to school, and not a move you could get out of him, and him as manly looking, and this wee sailor suit as smart looking on him, and—and—and at the heel of the hunt I had to go with him myself,
200		the two of us, hand in hand, as happy as larks—we were that happy, Madge—and him dancing and chatting beside me—mind?—you couldn't get a word in edge-ways with all the chatting he used to go through . . . Maybe, Madge, maybe it's because I could have been his grandfather, eh?
205	MADGE:	I don't know.
	S.B.:	I was too old for her, Madge, eh?
	MADGE:	I don't know. They're a new race—a new world.
	S.B.:	[*Leaving.*] In the wee sailor suit—all the chatting he used to go through . . . I don't know either . . .

Question

Make a detailed study of the dramatic techniques used in this extract to give us access to

- the internal conflict Gar is experiencing
- S.B.'s feelings about Gar's imminent departure.

[Turn over

Section 4—Reading the Media

You must answer **one question only** in this section.

Category A—Film

1. With reference to key sequences from **one** or **more than one** film, assess the effectiveness of the cinematic techniques — camera, lighting, editing, mise-en-scène — employed to engage the feelings of the audience.

2. With detailed reference to **one** or **more than one** film, discuss how **one** director manipulates audience reactions **either** by adhering to **or** by rejecting a genre's conventions.

Category B—Television

3. "*The kind of television drama that should still have a place today is drama that challenges the ideas, the values, the assumptions of the audience.*"

   What evidence have you found that recent television drama (a series, a serial or a single play) "*challenges*" its audience?

4. "*The job of public service broadcasting is to present fact and truth with clarity, dispassion and neutrality, however inconvenient or dismaying much of that information may be.*"

   Discuss the extent to which this ideal is realised in news **or** current affairs **or** documentary television.

Category C—Radio

5. "*As a secondary medium, radio insinuates itself into our daily routine; radio goes with us.*"

   Discuss the various means by which radio exploits its role as a secondary medium.

6. How does radio compensate for, or even exploit, sound broadcasting's lack of a visual dimension? In your answer you should make reference to at least **two** genres of radio, one of which may be radio commercials.

[Turn over for Category D on *Page forty*

Category D—Print journalism

7. *"The popular press reduces major news events to a formula narrative in which character is the most important element."*

Discuss with reference to **one** or **more than one** newspaper's coverage of a major news event.

8. In this question you are presented with an extract from the newspaper coverage of the 2002 Conservative Party Conference by *The Daily Telegraph* (*Page forty-one*).

Make a detailed study of the extract in which you should consider:

- the image of Theresa May in terms of camera angle and distance, cropping and framing
- the headline and the caption which accompany this image
- the cultural codes which establish the representation of female politicians
- the ideological assumptions about gender, politics and power contained both in the image and in the text of the extract.

A stiletto in the Tories' heart

BY GEORGE JONES
POLITICAL EDITOR
AND ANDREW SPARROW

THE Tories must get rid of their image as the "nasty party" and spread their appeal beyond Middle England, Theresa May, the party chairman, told the annual conference yesterday in an unusually outspoken opening address.

She made clear the scale of the task facing Conservatives if they were to regain power. In the past the party had indulged in "petty feuding" and "personal sniping", "demonised minorities" and twice gone to the country appearing unrepentant and unattractive.

The chairman's address is usually a rallying call to the faithful, laced with jokes about their political opponents. But Mrs May, appointed in July with a brief to speed up party reform, broke with precedent in Bournemouth to deliver a hard-hitting lecture on the unfavourable way they were viewed by many voters.

Rarely has a party been told in such blunt terms by its own leadership how unpopular it was. But many of her comments were in line with a You-Gov poll in *The Daily Telegraph* yesterday, which showed the party was disconnected from modern Britain.

Mrs May praised Tony Blair for the action he was taking to disarm Saddam Hussein – rejecting criticism from senior Tories that Iain Duncan-Smith, the party leader, should be more critical over possible military action.

She received polite applause, but Mr Duncan-Smith sat prominently in the front row in a clear signal of support for her message that the party must change.

In an interview with Graham Turner published in *The Daily Telegraph* today, Mr Duncan-Smith underlines the huge task facing him in reviving Tory fortunes after two landslide defeats.

When told a few months ago that it hardly seemed respectable to vote Tory, he replied: "You can forget the 'hardly'. It isn't respectable."

Mr Duncan-Smith said they entered the last election as the sort of party "you wouldn't admit among consenting adults that you'd voted for". Even now they were not regarded as an alternative government.

The Tories had to show people the party was broadening "that we have human beings running it, that we are not an absurd sect". Mrs May's speech was part of a strategy by the Tory leadership to show that the party was putting the past behind it and concentrating on issues of concern to voters.

The run-up to the conference was dominated by headlines on Edwina Currie's affair with John Major, Jeffrey Archer's prison diary and rumblings about Mr Duncan-Smith's leadership.

Mrs May, dressed in a black trouser suit against a new set intended to demonstrate that the Tories had become more open, acknowledged that they had been damaged by recent scandals.

Without naming anyone, Mrs May said: "A number of politicians have behaved disgracefully and then compounded their offences by trying to evade responsibility. We know who they are. Let's face it, some of them have stood on this platform.

Look sharp: Theresa May cuts a dash on the conference platform in £225 mock leopard-skin stilettos and bell-bottom trousers

"Some Tories have tried to make political capital by demonising minorities instead of showing confidence in all the citizens of our country.

"Some Tories have indulged themselves in petty feuding or personal sniping instead of getting behind a leader who is doing an enormous amount to change a party which has suffered two massive landslide defeats.

"Twice we went to the country unchanged, unrepentant, just plain unattractive. And twice we got slaughtered."

She said that soldiering on to the next election without radical change was not an option. The party's base was "too narrow and so, occasionally, are our sympathies. You know what some people call us? The nasty party".

That was unfair, she said, but the Tories could only shed that image by avoiding behaviour and attitudes that played into the hands of opponents. "No more glib moralising, no more hypocritical finger wagging. We need to reach out to all areas of our society."

Local Tory associations must move with the times and select more women and ethnic minority candidates, rather than white, public school-educated males.

Her message was underlined by Oliver Letwin, the shadow home secretary, who said the Conservative Party looked "weird" because it has so few women MPs.

Category E—Advertising

9. *"Advertising does not lead—it follows; both the product and the advertisement reflect society."*

Discuss a range of both press and television advertisements in the light of this assertion.

10. Examine carefully the Dulux paint advertisement from *The Observer Magazine*, 2003 (*Page forty-three*).

How effectively does this advertisement convey the message of the advertiser?

In your answer, you should consider the following:

- the use of comic strip/picture story conventions
- the use of technical codes, especially camera angle and distance and lighting in the frames
- the cultural codes in the representation of the male and the female
- the assumptions about gender roles and nationality, and the ideological basis of these
- the role of the product in the narrative.

[*END OF QUESTION PAPER*]

[BLANK PAGE]

2005 | Advanced Higher

[BLANK PAGE]

X115/701

NATIONAL QUALIFICATIONS 2005

FRIDAY, 13 MAY
1.00 PM – 4.00 PM

ENGLISH
ADVANCED HIGHER

There are four sections in this paper.

Depending on the options you have chosen, you must answer **one** or **two** questions.

If you have submitted a Creative Writing folio, you must answer only **one** question.

Otherwise, you must answer **two** questions.

If you are required to answer only **one question**

- it must be taken from **Section 1—Literary Study**
- you must leave the examination room **after 1 hour 30 minutes**.

If you are required to answer **two questions**

- your first must be taken from **Section 1—Literary Study**
- your second must be taken from **a different section**
- each answer must be written in **a separate answer booklet**
- the maximum time allowed for any question is **1 hour 30 minutes**.

You must identify each question you attempt by indicating clearly

- **the title of the section** from which the question has been taken
- **the number of the question** within that section.

You must also write inside the front cover of your Literary Study answer booklet

- **the topic** of your Specialist Study (Dissertation)
- **the texts** used in your Specialist Study (Dissertation).

©

Section 1—Literary Study

This section is **mandatory** for all candidates.

You must answer **one question only** in this section.

DRAMA

1. Bridie

"***The Anatomist*** *and* ***Mr Bolfry*** *are essentially arenas for argument, for dispute, for debate.*"

Discuss.

2. Byrne

"*What makes* ***The Slab Boys Trilogy*** *remarkable is Byrne's blending of stereotypical characters with characters of depth and complexity.*"

How far do you agree?

3. Chekhov

Discuss the importance of symbolism in *The Cherry Orchard* **or** in *Uncle Vanya* **or** in both plays.

4. Glover

Examine Glover's treatment of issues of social class in **each** of the specified texts.

5. Lindsay

Analyse the principal means by which Lindsay dramatises political issues in *Ane Satyre of the Thrie Estaitis.*

6. Lochhead

What effects are created by Lochhead's variation of tone and mood in *Mary Queen of Scots Got Her Head Chopped Off* **or** in *Dracula* **or** in both plays?

7. McLellan

Compare and contrast McLellan's handling of dramatic structure in *Jamie the Saxt* with his handling of dramatic structure in *The Flouers o Edinburgh.*

8. Pinter

"*Pinter's characters evade direct communication with others: they do not want to listen, or to understand, but want to be listened to, or at least to be allowed to speak.*"

Keeping this quotation in mind, discuss the nature and function of Pinter's dialogue.

9. Shakespeare

"*In Shakespeare, tragedy does not derive from the fatal flaws of heroes, but from the fundamental flaws of the worlds the heroes inhabit.*"

How far, in your view, does this assertion apply to *Hamlet* **and** to *King Lear*?

10. Shaw

To what extent is conflict between spiritual and worldly power central to the dramatic impact of **each** of the specified texts?

11. Stoppard

How effective do you find the endings of *Rosencrantz and Guildenstern are Dead* **and** *Arcadia*?

12. Williams

"*Williams's plays depend upon the skilful creation of dramatic tension.*"

How far do you agree?

In your answer you should make detailed reference to key scenes from *The Glass Menagerie* **and** *A Streetcar Named Desire.*

POETRY

13. Chaucer

"*Much of Chaucer's success is due to the way in which he builds up his characters by an accumulation of closely observed significant detail.*"

Examine Chaucer's characterisation by reference to a range of characters from *The General Prologue* **and** from **one** or **two** of the *Tales*.

14. Coleridge

With reference to **two** or **three** of his poems, discuss the means by which Coleridge creates a profound sense of loss.

15. Donne and the metaphysical poets

"*One of the strengths of the metaphysical poets is the skill with which they bring to their religious poetry so much experience that is not in itself religious.*"

Discuss with reference to **three** or **four** religious poems by **one** or **more than one** metaphysical poet.

[Turn over

16. Duffy

Read the following poem carefully, and then answer the question that follows it.

CRUSH

The older she gets,
the more she awakes
with somebody's face strewn in her head
like petals which once made a flower.

5 What everyone does
is sit by a desk
and stare at the view, till the time
where they live reappears. Mostly in words.

Imagine a girl
10 turning to see
love stand by a window, taller,
clever, anointed with sudden light.

Yes, like an angel then,
to be truthful now.
15 At first a secret, erotic, mute;
today a language she cannot recall.

And we're all owed joy,
sooner or later.
The trick's to remember whenever
20 it was, or to see it coming.

Make a detailed analysis of Duffy's treatment of love in this poem **and** go on to compare her treatment of love in this poem with her treatment of love in **one** or **two** other poems.

17. Dunbar

Discuss Dunbar's use of traditional images and symbols—for example, heraldic, religious, natural—in **three** or **four** poems.

18. Dunn

Examine the effects created by Dunn's use of the persona of a detached observer in **three** or **four** poems.

19. Fergusson

"*At the heart of Fergusson's poetry lies an exuberant celebration of the rich diversity of human life.*"

Discuss with reference to **three** or **four** poems.

20. Heaney

Either

(*a*) Make a close critical analysis of the following poem.

The Strand at Lough Beg

In Memory of Colum McCartney

All round this little island, on the strand
Far down below there, where the breakers strive
Grow the tall rushes from the oozy sand.
—Dante, *Purgatorio, I, 100–3*

Leaving the white glow of filling stations
And a few lonely streetlamps among fields
You climbed the hills toward Newtownhamilton
Past the Fews Forest, out beneath the stars—
5 Along the road, a high, bare pilgrim's track
Where Sweeney fled before the bloodied heads,
Goat-beards and dogs' eyes in a demon pack
Blazing out of the ground, snapping and squealing.
What blazed ahead of you? A faked road block?
10 The red lamp swung, the sudden brakes and stalling
Engine, voices, heads hooded and the cold-nosed gun?
Or in your driving mirror, tailing headlights
That pulled out suddenly and flagged you down
Where you weren't known and far from what you knew:
15 The lowland clays and waters of Lough Beg,
Church Island's spire, its soft treeline of yew.

There you used to hear guns fired behind the house
Long before rising time, when duck shooters
Haunted the marigolds and bulrushes,
20 But still were scared to find spent cartridges,
Acrid, brassy, genital, ejected,
On your way across the strand to fetch the cows.
For you and yours and yours and mine fought the shy,
Spoke an old language of conspirators
25 And could not crack the whip or seize the day:
Big-voiced scullions, herders, feelers round
Haycocks and hindquarters, talkers in byres,
Slow arbitrators of the burial ground.

Across that strand of ours the cattle graze
30 Up to their bellies in an early mist
And now they turn their unbewildered gaze
To where we work our way through squeaking sedge
Drowning in dew. Like a dull blade with its edge
Honed bright, Lough Beg half shines under the haze.
35 I turn because the sweeping of your feet
Has stopped behind me, to find you on your knees
With blood and roadside muck in your hair and eyes,

Then kneel in front of you in brimming grass
And gather up cold handfuls of the dew
40 To wash you, cousin. I dab you clean with moss
Fine as the drizzle out of a low cloud.
I lift you under the arms and lay out flat.
With rushes that shoot green again, I plait
Green scapulars to wear over your shroud.

Or

(*b*) Make a comparative evaluation of Heaney's achievement in **three** or **four** of his elegies on the death of friends or family members.

You may, if you wish, use *The Strand at Lough Beg* in your answer.

21. Hopkins

What, for you, are the most distinctive aspects of Hopkins's poetic treatment of spiritual crisis?

In your answer you should make close reference to **three** or **four** of his poems.

22. Morgan

"*Morgan's very best poems are those that treat human relationships with remarkable warmth and compassion.*"

In the light of this statement, make a detailed study of Morgan's treatment of human relationships in **three** or **four** poems.

23. Plath

"*In Plath's major work, her preoccupation with death is always accompanied by a recurring theme of rebirth, of physical and spiritual regeneration.*"

Discuss with reference to **three** or **four** poems.

24. The Scottish Ballads

Read the following poem carefully, and then answer the question that follows it.

THE BONNIE HOOSE O AIRLIE

It fell on a day, on a bonnie simmer's day
When the corn was ripe and yellow,
That there fell oot a great dispute
Between Argyll and Airlie.

5 Noo the lady looked owre yon high castle waa,
And oh, but she sighed sairly
Whan she saa Argyll and aa he's men
Come tae plunder the bonnie hoose o Airlie.

"Come doon, come doon, Lady Marg'ret," he says,
10 "Come doon and kiss me fairly,
Or gin the mornin's clear daylight
I'll no leave a stannin stane in Airlie."

"I'll no come doon, you false Argyll,
Nor wid I kiss thee fairly:
15 I widnae kiss the fause Argyll
Though ye widnae leave a stannin stane in Airlie.

Noo if my guid lord had been at hame
As he's awaa wi Chairlie,
There widnae come a Campbell frae Argyll
20 Dared tae trod upon the bonnie green o Airlie.

For I have borne him seven bonnie sons
But the eighth yin has never seen his daddy,
But had I jist as mony owre again
They wid aa be men for Chairlie."

25 Noo Argyll in a rage he kennled sic a lowe
That it rose tae lift red an clearly,
An poor Lady Marg'ret and aa her weans
They were smothered in the dark reek o Airlie.

"Draa yir dirks, draa yir dirks!" cried the brave Lochiel;
30 "Unsheathe yir swords!" cried Chairlie,
"An we'll kennle sic a lowe roond the fause Argyll
An we'll licht it wi a spark oot'n Airlie!"

Analyse the means by which a profound sense of tragedy is created in this ballad **and** in two other Scottish ballads.

PROSE FICTION

25. Achebe

Examine the means by which Achebe explores the role of women within the societies he depicts in his fiction.

26. Austen

"*After all her ironies, wit and satire, reconciliation after estrangement is the central experience that seems to lie at the heart of Austen's novels.*"

Discuss with reference to *Emma* **and** *Persuasion.*

27. Dickens

"*Childhood—both as subject and as a way of seeing the world—is at the heart of Dickens's fiction.*"

Discuss with reference **either** to *Bleak House* **or** to *Great Expectations*.

28. Forster

*Read the following extract from **Howards End**, Chapter 22, and then answer one of the questions that follow it (Page nine).*

Margaret greeted her lord with peculiar tenderness on the morrow. Mature as he was, she might yet be able to help him to the building of the rainbow bridge that should connect the prose in us with the passion. Without it we are meaningless fragments, half monks, half beasts, unconnected arches that have never joined into a
5 man. With it love is born, and alights on the highest curve, glowing against the grey, sober against the fire. Happy the man who sees from either aspect the glory of these outspread wings. The roads of his soul lie clear, and he and his friends shall find easy-going.

It was hard-going in the roads of Mr. Wilcox's soul. From boyhood he had
10 neglected them. "I am not a fellow who bothers about my own inside." Outwardly he was cheerful, reliable, and brave; but within, all had reverted to chaos, ruled, so far as it was ruled at all, by an incomplete asceticism. Whether as boy, husband, or widower, he had always the sneaking belief that bodily passion is bad, a belief that is desirable only when held passionately. Religion had confirmed him. The words that were read aloud
15 on Sunday to him and other respectable men were the words that had once kindled the souls of St. Catharine and St. Francis into a white-hot hatred of the carnal. He could not be as the saints and love the Infinite with a seraphic ardour, but he could be a little ashamed of loving a wife. "Amabat, amare timebat." And it was here that Margaret hoped to help him.

20 It did not seem so difficult. She need trouble him with no gift of her own. She would only point out the salvation that was latent in his own soul, and in the soul of every man. Only connect! That was the whole of her sermon. Only connect the prose and the passion, and both will be exalted, and human love will be seen at its height. Live in fragments no longer. Only connect, and the beast and the monk, robbed of the
25 isolation that is life to either, will die.

Nor was the message difficult to give. It need not take the form of a good "talking". By quiet indications the bridge would be built and span their lives with beauty.

But she failed. For there was one quality in Henry for which she was never prepared, however much she reminded herself of it: his obtuseness. He simply did not notice
30 things, and there was no more to be said. He never noticed that Helen and Frieda were hostile, or that Tibby was not interested in currant plantations; he never noticed the lights and shades that exist in the greyest conversation, the finger-posts, the milestones, the collisions, the illimitable views. Once—on another occasion—she scolded him about it. He was puzzled, but replied with a laugh: "My motto is Concentrate. I've no
35 intention of frittering away my strength on that sort of thing." "It isn't frittering away the strength," she protested. "It's enlarging the space in which you may be strong." He answered: "You're a clever little woman, but my motto's Concentrate." And this morning he concentrated with a vengeance.

Either

(*a*) Analyse the means by which Forster explores the characters of Margaret and Henry in this extract **and** elsewhere in the novel.

Or

(*b*) In what ways are characters' attempts to "*connect the prose . . . with the passion*" (line 3) important **either** in *Howards End* **or** in *A Passage to India* **or** in both novels?

29. Galloway

"*Each of Galloway's novels boasts an impressive range of comic elements, in style and language, in action, in characterisation.*"

Discuss the contribution made by a range of comic elements to the effectiveness of **each** of the specified texts.

30. Gray

Analyse Gray's fictional representation of Glasgow **either** in *Lanark* **or** in *Lanark* **and** in *Poor Things*.

31. Gunn

Make a detailed analysis of Gunn's treatment of the rites of passage experienced by Kenn in *Highland River* **or** by Finn in *The Silver Darlings*.

32. Hardy

Hardy asserted that "*the best tragedy—highest tragedy in short—is that of the worthy encompassed by the inevitable.*"

In light of this assertion, discuss Hardy's treatment of "the worthy encompassed by the inevitable" in *Tess of the d'Urbervilles* **or** in *The Mayor of Casterbridge* **or** in both novels.

33. Hogg

Discuss the significance of setting—physical, historical, cultural—in *The Private Memoirs and Confessions of a Justified Sinner* **or** in **two** or **three** short stories.

34. Joyce

Discuss Joyce's treatment of the tensions of family life in *Dubliners* **and** in *A Portrait of the Artist as a Young Man*.

35. Spark

How successful do you find Spark's combination of the realistic and the fantastic in *The Prime of Miss Jean Brodie* **and** in *The Girls of Slender Means*?

[Turn over

36. Stevenson

Analyse some of the principal means by which Stevenson explores the mental state and the motives of his main protagonists in *The Strange Case of Dr Jekyll and Mr Hyde* **and** in *Weir of Hermiston*.

PROSE NON-FICTION

37. Autobiography

Examine the means by which any **two** of the specified autobiographies handle difficult, even traumatic, experiences in the lives of the authors.

38. Autobiography

How successful are any **two** of the specified autobiographies in avoiding sentimentality in the treatment of childhood experiences and relationships?

39. Travel Writing

"*Travel writing is addressed to readers at home and is, in the main, about journeys, places and people abroad; so representations of 'otherness' and attempts to translate these into familiar terms are major concerns of the travel narrative.*"

How successful are any **two** of the specified texts in their representations and translations of "otherness"?

40. Travel Writing

Examine the nature and function of humour in any **two** of the specified texts.

41. Writing about Scotland

How far could any **one** of the specified texts be described as an elegy for the loss or the passing of a way of life?

42. Writing about Scotland

The dustjacket of the first edition of Edwin Muir's *Scottish Journey* (1935) stated that: "*No reader thinking to find the Scotland of the tourist's delight should open this book*".

To what extent is *Scottish Journey* **or** any **one** of the other specified texts concerned primarily with stripping away comforting illusions about the Scotland of its day?

Section 2—Language Study

You must answer **one question only** in this section.

Topic A—The use of English in a particular geographical area

1. "*As English becomes an increasingly global language, the distinctiveness of local varieties has become eroded.*"

Discuss the above statement with reference to a particular variety of English that you have studied.

2. Explain the reasons—social, linguistic, historical, geographical—for the development of a particular variety of English that you have studied.

Topic B—Variations in the use of English related to social class

3. Give a detailed account of the procedures you would follow to investigate the relationship of language use to social class.

4. In the two transcriptions given below, identify and discuss critically the features that would cause you to label one as "middle-class" speech and the other as "working-class" speech.

The transcription of each conversation is light.

First transcription

A: that is skirlie

B: I've never had that

A: oh well Jock it's awfully tasty

B: I've heard of it

but I've never tasted it

A: if you even want

to put say a chopped onion and some dried fruit in it

it makes a—like a white pudding

that you buy in the butcher

and slice that sort of thing

we used to—

one of my favourites was a haggis a sweet haggis

which mother made

sheep's stomach bags

which of course you could get from the butcher

it was always a big one and a little one of about that size

and she made this marvellous mixture of oatmeal beef suet chopped

seasoning salt and pepper and usually currants

and this was all put into this—these two bags
they were all sterilised and clean and scraped and sewn with a big darning needle and a bit of thread
and then they were boiled
and then after they were cooked
they were put in this warm cupboard
we had where—
the kitchen range and the pipes went through a nice cupboard
where you had biscuit tins and all sorts of things
that kept close to it
and this was kept in there in a big ashet

Second transcription

X: they had grazing doon at Bargennie
and this day it was an Irishman
that was working aboot the place
and the two of us was to go to Dailly
to pick up half a dozen horse and a dozen bullocks
and we went up to Dalrymple
to get the train
and we got the train
and I had aye heard tell o the burning pit
so I must see this burning pit
I seen the burning pit aw right
I got a spark in my eye
and anyway I stertit—
the worst thing I could have done
I sterted rubbing it
so anyway we got the horse and the beasts
and set oot
we werenae too bad
until we came to Meybole [= Maybole]
and when we came doon to the bottom of Meybole
the blooming things took away doon from Crosshill
and we couldnae leave the horse
anyway we got them aw thegither again
and set oot

Topic C—Variations in the use of English related to gender

5. "*Many of the differences observed in the talk of men and women arise from the distinctive norms, conceptions and interpretations of friendly conversation that they learn in segregated subcultures (ie boys' and girls' peer groups).*"

   What linguistic differences are thought to arise from boys' and girls' learning to converse in single-sex peer groups? How plausible do you find the argument that learning to converse in single-sex peer groups accounts for these differences?

6. Some linguists claim that women use more standard or "prestige" pronunciations than men from the same social class. Discuss the evidence for and against such a claim.

Topic D—The linguistic characteristics of informal conversation

For both questions on this topic, consider the following text. It is a transcription of an informal conversational exchange between "Heather" and "Don", two young American adults.

It contains the following transcription conventions.

Square brackets indicate that utterances are simultaneous.
Numbers in round brackets indicate the length of a pause in seconds.
Words in round brackets indicate that the transcriber is unsure of exact wording.
Empty round brackets indicate that the transcriber cannot make out what was said.
Punctuation: a full-stop indicates falling intonation; a question-mark represents rising intonation.
Breathing indicators: hh indicates breathing out; .hh indicates breathing in.
Colons indicate that the previous syllable is prolonged
Underlining indicates that the part of the utterance is heavily stressed.
Equal signs indicate that no time elapses between parts of an utterance.

1	Heather:	He shoulda bought a water bed.
2	Don:	Na::
3	Heather:	Much more comfort[able
4	Don:	[.hh I got my uh (1.2) I did get my tax forms today
5	Heather:	Yea
6	Don:	Yea I walked inta the post office an' mail my thing and I took one of everything hhh
7	Heather:	I did too = I took two of everything.
8	Don:	For me?
9	Heather:	Yea
10	Don:	That's my baby
11		(1.0)
12	Don:	How was school today?

13	Heather:	Okay
14		(3.6)
15	Don:	Hhhh Just okay?
16	Heather:	Ayup
17	Don:	Why what happened?
18	Heather:	Nothin. It was kinda boring. We left for lunch though
19	Don:	Who did
20	Heather:	Me and Maria an' Sean an' ( ) an' Max Clancey
21	Don:	Sean who?
22	Heather:	Sean ah (1.0) Peters. Maria's—You know Abruzzi
23	Don:	Yeah
24	Heather:	Maria's new boyfriend.
25		(2.4)
26	Don:	And who?
27	Heather:	A:h his best friend Max
28		(2.0)
29	Heather:	We just went to Dunkin's I had to have a croissant
30	Don:	Yea well you better tell Max that uh::
31	Heather:	<u>Max</u> has a girlfriend
32	Don:	Yea
33	Heather:	Plus he (has disgusting earrings)
34		(4.0)
35	Don:	Hhhh Me and Vic did a lota talking tonight

7. Discuss the ways in which the social roles and identities of each speaker are enacted through this exchange.

8. Discuss the principal issues involved in transcribing speech, and explain why it is useful to have the kind of detailed information that is shown here.

Topic E—The linguistic characteristics of political communication

9. "*The task of political discourse analysis is to relate linguistic behaviour to political behaviour.*"

Discuss this statement with reference to your own study of political communication.

10. The following passage is the opening section of a keynote speech entitled ***Time for a Change*** given by David McLetchie, leader of the Scottish Conservatives, to the Scottish Conservative & Unionist Party Rally on Friday, November 29th, 2002, at Dynamic Earth, Edinburgh. It took place five months before the May 2003 Scottish Parliamentary election. For ease of reference, the paragraphs have been numbered.

Make a detailed analysis of the linguistic characteristics of this passage. You should examine as many of the following as you consider appropriate:

- the degree of formality
- the choice of vocabulary
- the degree of grammatical complexity
- the characterisation of rival parties
- the use of humour
- the characteristics of spoken and written discourse evident here.

Time for a Change

[1] Anyone would think there was an election in the offing!

[2] Well, ladies and gentlemen, let nobody be in any doubt. We are ready for these elections. We are raring to go and we are hungry for success.

[3] The signs are positive. Forget the opinion polls—clipboards don't count. It's real voters in real elections who matter. And out there in the real world, in council by-elections all over Scotland in the last three years, we have held every Tory ward and gained 8 from our opponents. Not just from Labour, but from the Liberal Democrats, from the SNP and from the Independents for good measure. This year alone, we have gained two wards from the Lib Dems and one from the SNP. We have taken on all comers and we've won. It's a record to be proud of. The Scottish Conservatives are alive and kicking and I pay tribute to everyone involved in those campaigns.

[4] We have achieved much since May 1997. But there's still a long way to go. Our ultimate objective is to be a party of government in Scotland again at all levels. This May, we can take a big step forward—more Conservative councillors, more Conservative-run councils and a bigger presence in the Scottish Parliament. All this is within our grasp.

[5] If you seek any further motivation in the coming campaign, then just look across the road. We meet this evening in the shadow of the new Parliament building at Holyrood. "Follyrood" is the perfect symbol of the waste, incompetence and perverse priorities of the last 4 years of Labour/Lib Dem rule. The cost has risen from £40 million to nearly £400 million. There is still no date for completion and as a result we are told that the Scottish Parliament may have to meet in a pub. It should be called "the last chance saloon".

[6] Holyrood is both a farce and a national scandal and the guilty must be brought to book. The First Minister said last week that it has been the "single biggest disappointment of devolution". For once, he's right. But what a brass neck. For Holyrood is truly the house that Jack built.

[7] It was Labour which promised it would cost only £40 million. Labour which chose the Holyrood site. Labour which rejected a fixed price tender. Labour which ruled out PFI. Labour MSPs and their Lib Dem lackeys who have voted on 4 separate occasions in the Parliament to proceed with this project. And it is the Labour and Lib Dem Scottish Government which continues to abdicate its responsibility and carries on signing the blank cheques—money with which we could and should have built schools, hospitals and roads.

[8] Nothing, absolutely nothing, better illustrates why Scotland needs a change of government next year than that building.

Topic F—The linguistic characteristics of tabloid journalism

11. "*Neither the content of the news nor the language used to express it is value free.*"

With reference to tabloid journalism you have studied, exemplify and discuss the above statement.

12. Read *The Sun* editorial of Monday, February 9, 2004 (see *Page seventeen*) and explain how the form and content of the text are used to present people and events. Identify how language is used to establish and maintain a relationship with the reader. In particular, consider what assumptions are built into the text about the views of the reader.

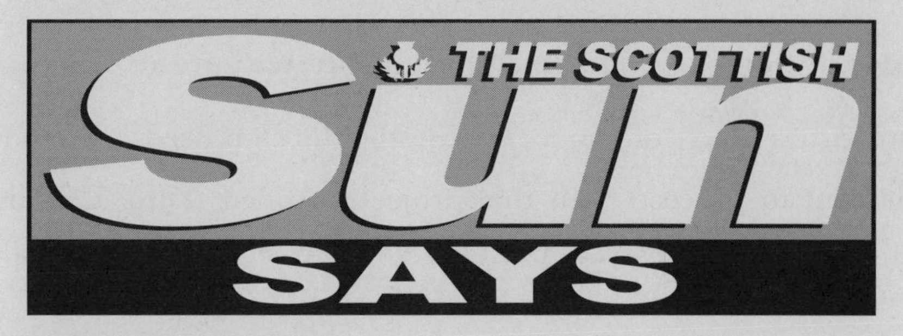

Hits and myths

CRIME figures, by their very nature, live in a shadowy world of half-truths, myths and inter-gang rivalry.

Attacks on each other become gangland hits, petty squabbles become turf wars.

Squalid dealers court the notoriety that elevates them into "crime barons" and "underworld lords".

But throw guns into the mix and the stakes are raised to an unacceptably dangerous level.

There is **NO** suggestion that the two victims of the weekend's two shootings in Glasgow had any criminal background.

But the two men wounded in a pub shooting in Glasgow last week both had links to suspected crime figures.

There is another half-truth—that gang shootings don't matter if the crooks only pick on each other.

But police MUST crack down on gun crime — with tough sentencing in the courts to back them up — before innocents are caught in the crossfire.

Compo culture

NO case better illustrates the extremes of the compensation culture.

Anthony Grimes set fire to himself in prison and was horribly burned.

Worse, he put a pregnant nurse in hospital and left 20 staff needing medical treatment.

Whose fault was it?

Common sense dictates it was no one's but his own.

But under our ridiculous system, he gets £5,000 of taxpayers' money so he can sue the Prison Service.

He blames them for letting him set himself alight.

Have you heard anything wackier than that? We haven't.

Well said, sir!

PRINCE Charles didn't have to go to Basra.

It was his own idea, as Colonel-in-Chief of the Parachute Regiment, to visit the troops in Iraq.

He put himself at risk, and meeting the squaddies will undoubtedly have boosted morale.

He told them: "You are a remarkable bunch."

We couldn't agree more, Charles.

Big spender

TEENAGER Tom Smith's spending spree on his dad's credit card was remarkable.

He blew £12,000 on designer gear and high living in four days.

He can always get a job in Madrid.

As Posh and Becks' financial adviser.

Topic G—The use of Scots in a particular geographical area

13. "Dinna chuck bruck" is a contemporary Shetlandic sign used to encourage people not to throw litter.

From your own research, describe in detail how any geographical area in Scotland has maintained its linguistic richness into the 21st century.

14. Explain the reasons—social, linguistic, historical, geographical—for the development of a particular variety of Scots that you have studied.

Topic H—The linguistic characteristics of Scots as used in informal conversation

For both questions on this topic (see *Page twenty*), consider the following text. It is a conversation between a man in his forties (Speaker 1) and three women in their sixties and seventies (Speakers 2, 3 and 4).

It contains the following transcription codes.

Overlapping speech in conversations Where two speakers talk at once, the person who began speaking first has the tags <INT> </INT> for "interrupted" marked around the section of his or her speech that is being spoken over and the second speaker has the tags <OVR> </OVR> for "overlapping" marked round his or her speech while the first speaker continues to talk.

False starts Where a speaker begins to say a phrase and abruptly re-starts and re-phrases what he or she was going to say, the tag <FS> is used in between the false start and the new phrase.

Personal and place names Personal names are marked <FN> for first name, <SN> for surname, and <FNSN> for first name plus surname. Place names are shown as <PN>.

Inaudible speech Speech that cannot be described is marked as <NA> XXXX </NA>.

Non-verbal features Laughter and other non-verbal features are shown as <NV> laughs </NV>.

Speaker 1: What was the difference between the the big school and the junior school? I mean what kinda ... ?

Speaker 2: Well then it was like i- eh movin now. Ye had a different teacher for each subject, whereas ye had the same teacher for the f- the whole year <INT>... That eh </INT>

Speaker 3: <OVR>Ye know,</OVR> for the first two years ye went tae school ye had the same teacher. I'd a Miss <SN>. And eh, I remember she got ma- she <FS> we got word she was gettin married. And I thought, "How's it <FS> what's an old woman like her gettin married for?" But she must have been oh twenty-three or twenty-four. But to me, at between five and seven, she was an old woman. And eh, then ye went up to the big school, and ye started getting different teachers for arithmetic and eh different things like that. And I remember I was off a year, off the school a full year wae bein in hospital — I had scarlet fever and one thing and another. And eh . . . I was five months in the hospital wae scarlet fever.

Speaker 1: Uhuh.

Speaker 3: And then I was o- <FS> Then I sprained ma ankle, and then I took somethin else ... I was off a full year. An eh I went up back to the school and the the headmaster said, "Och we'll just put her in her old class, she'll no be long. She'll catch up."

Speaker 1: Mhm

Speaker 3: ... And I got this eh teach-, Miss <SN>. And the first day there spellin was never ma strong point and she gave me the belt right up tae there for havein four le- four eh spellins wrong. And ma mother went up, and gave her oh what for, ye know

Speaker 1: Aye

Speaker 3: ... I got the belt every day that I was in her class <INT> ... Every day </INT> she took took it out o me that woman ...

Speaker 2: <OVR><laughing> Whether ye needed it or not! <NV> laughs </NV></OVR>

Speaker 3: Aye, and then ye got another teacher for <FS> ye then ye went tae cookery.

Speaker 1: Aye.

Speaker 3: Now they had a cookery <FS> <INT> when ye went tae cookery</INT>

Speaker 2: <OVR>Ye'd tae go tae <PN> Academy </OVR> for f- cookery

Speaker 3: Naw, naw.

Speaker 2: I did!

Speaker 3: We we had a cookery cla- <FS> a a cookery bit under the clinic, remember th-?

Speaker 2: Oh right, we went for laundry to that <PN> Academy.

Speaker 3: Right, first time ye went for laundry, ye went <INT> tae Catholic school.</INT>

Speaker 1: <OVR><?>Did you say</?> you had a class on laundry?</OVR>

Speaker 2: Ye had a class in roi- laundry. And ye had to take articles fae the house <INT> and ye washed them. </INT>

Speaker 3: <OVR>A hanky!</OVR> ... <INT>A lady's and a gent's hanky</INT>

Speaker 4: <OVR><NA>XXX</NA>the first thing</OVR>

Speaker 2: Yes.

Speaker 3: A lady's and a gent's hanky, and that was a whole lesson. And ye had the boiling, the<INT>bleaching and the blueing!</INT>

Speaker 2: <OVR>The blueing, the blueing.</OVR> and the bleaching!

Speaker 4: Mhm.

Speaker 3: So ye had tae dae this wae these two hankies.

Speaker 1: Ye were taught well!

Speaker 2: <NV>laughs</NV>

Speaker 3: And then they went up on the pulley.

Speaker 4: Mhm

Speaker 1: Mhm

Speaker 3: In the the class room, the- they'd all these pulleys, ye know, for dryin the <INT> clothes... </INT> So, it lay up there for a week.

Speaker 4: <OVR><NA>XXX</NA></OVR>

Speaker 2: Yeh, and you ironed it! <NV>laughs</NV>

Speaker 3: And then, the next week, ye were taught how tae iron it and fold it.

Speaker 4: Wae the great big heavy irons.

Speaker 3: Aye.

Speaker 2: Uhuh.

Speaker 3: The big ones that heated on a hob, ye know a flat iron

Speaker 1: How many people were in a class ironing?

Speaker 3: Oh aboot, maybe aboot twenty odds.

Speaker 4: Oh aye your whole a whole class

Speaker 3: Aye, uhuh. And then ye went for cookery ... <INT>and ye worked in pairs.</INT>

Speaker 2: <OVR>And then ye went for sewin</OVR>

Speaker 3: And then ye went for sewin. But ye got that in your own school, but for cookery <FS> the we had a cookery room, and eh they had tiny wee pots. But ye worked in pairs. And... my name was <SN>. And the one I had tae work wae was <FNSN>, and ye could have stuck her tae the wall; she was clarty. And eh... I wouldnae let her touch anything -

Speaker 1: Uhuh

Speaker 3: - that we were makin, because if she'd touched it I couldnae eat it.

Speaker 2: I never mind o cookin in twos

Speaker 3: Aye ye'd tae cook.

Speaker 2: Nah.

Speaker 3: Aye ye worked with pairs.

Speaker 2: Because I made lovely spongy scones.

Speaker 3: <NV>laughs</NV>

Speaker 2: I was the top in the class.

15. Explain how the four speakers interact and cooperate to develop the narrative.

16. Discuss the density and the use of Scots by the speakers.

Topic I—Variations in the use of Scots among older and younger people

17. "*Aye, thir were the days whan a wee man fae Govan cud walk intae a pub an order 'a hauf 'n' a hauf'–an be unnerstuid bi the barman.*"

Brent Hodgson in *Lallans* Nummer 62 Ware 2003

To what extent would you support the view that younger people no longer understand expressions such as "a hauf 'n' a hauf"?

Make reference to your own study of the use of Scots among older and younger people.

18. Discuss the issues involved in maintaining a traditional language variety in the modern world.

Topic J—Uses of Scots in the media

19. From a case study you have made, give an account of how Scots is used in one area of the media.

20. "*It really is **what** you say that matters, not **how** you say it.*"

Bill Leckie, in *The Sun,* Wednesday, October 1, 2003

The above statement was a response to comments made criticising the use of regional voices in broadcast media. Drawing on a range of examples from your study of the use of Scots in the media, consider whether you agree or disagree with the above statement.

Topic K—Uses of Scots in contemporary literature

21. Compare and contrast the Scots used in the following two extracts, Extract A and Extract B.

The extracts are selected from *The Fundamentals of New Caledonia* by David Nicol (2003). This novel is set in contemporary Edinburgh. The central character, Billy Budd, finds himself transported from the 21st century to the late 17th century at the time of the ill-fated Darien scheme in Central America. The language shifts from a contemporary Scots to a projected 17th century Scots.

EXTRACT A

FOLDING THEIR LETTER, I step out the broo at Torphichen Street, intae a smirr o drizzle. Six months at this game, and they're on my back. They want me tae join a jobclub, or some daft training scheme. I cut through Canning Street tae Shandwick Place, where the rain hammers down. By the time I reach the Caledonian hotel my UB40 is damp in the back pocket o my jeans. I plank it in my shirt, wi the letter.

Tin soldiers in kilts are birling around the Fraser's clock, as shoppers ebb in and out o the great department stores. Early tourists meld intae the dreich facade o Princes Street, while a lone piper brazens the rain. His back lilt bubbles, the drones splutter in the wet. A Japanese chucks siller in his case. Amazing Grace.

St. John's kirk is gloomy and grey. At the back o it a mural depicts the plight o the homeless. I would need tae come up wi some proof that I am actively seeking employment. It's the jobcentre the day.

But Princes Street's a scunner. So I cross over past McDonald's, giving the pickets a nod, turn up Castle Street and right along Rose Street, where the guff o a dozen pubs fills my nostrils. Fast walking then, through the pedestrian zone, behind Jenners, cutting along Meuse Lane tae reach St Andrew Street and the jobcentre.

Six months unemployed? says a poster in the window. Then you may be eligible for a stretch o slave labour. A credit on your *curriculum vitae*.

Butlins wants redcoats for Ayr.

A clammy warmth seeps under my skin as I saunter round by the miscellaneous vacancies board. I pick two likely jobs and scribble their numbers on the chit wi their blunt pencil, that I stick behind my ear, and draw a number. Sit in the comfy seat and wait. Here is the usual kind o crowd. The young mother wi her wean in a pushchair. A plooky boy.

EXTRACT B

THE CREW STUDE IDLE aneath the hott dripping sky, or alse loaft in the shrouds, not shewing the slightest inclinatioun tae float *Unicorn* up on the beach. *Sanct Andrew* wes lading ballast and watter on boord. Captain Robert Drummond wes daen likewise on *Caledonia*.

Ashoar the planters sett rumours in motioun, that the ship maisters hed formit ane pact tae abandon thaim. Even *Unicorn*, they sayd, sen her real Captain is tint, sal joyn wi the Commandore's designe, tae strike out for the Main and win proffits by reiving the Spainish fleet. Some men expresst their delight, considering this a just retributioun for our enemy's wrangs. Others sayd siccan ploys may bring the wrath o King Carlos and King William down on our heids.

Reports and contradixiouns, rumours and contrary rumours, washt about the hutts o New Edenbourg. Ilka morning ane thousan grim een peered out att the ships whar they laye. Seeing the masts in place, wi sails dousit, the planters gied a groan att the Captains' cowardice, or alse sighed in relief. In daytime, the slightest plash o an oar made ripples upon land. By night time, each antrin sound wes an object for scrutiny in shadowy hutts whair men hunkerit aneath the mean light o shell lamps and shark oyl lowe.

Hes the Comandore slippt his bough cable in the night?

Suppose wee awauken tae find New Caledonia left for wirsels?

How will wee fare?

As planters upon a foraign shoar, bot victalls that laye in the holds?

"Verra weel, and guid riddance!" sayd some.

"Wee will famish," sayd ithers.

"A swack in the teeth for Don Diego de los Rios Quesadas!" cryed some.

Can wee square up tae *Barliavento*? A mear hantle o gunns, and us wi toom wames.

Wee foregathert upon the haulf deck aneath the canaby. Davie sate on the capstan drum, whittling an auld block. Hirpling Jimmy lay on the pump dale making cradles wi a length o twine. Mister Craig performit ane jigg, a hornpipe, and an air. Syne he crumpelt his concertina, that made a grunt, and gied ower playing. He slumpit on a coyl o hawser, als tho the braith gaed out o him.

22. Examine and evaluate some of the strategies used by writers to represent the Scots language in contemporary literature.

Topic L—Uses of Scots in specialised fields

23. The use of Scots in place and street names has survived in some parts of Scotland but disappeared in others. For example, in one Scottish town "Baxter's Wynd" was replaced with "Baker Street", while in another, after discussion, a new street was named "Doocot Terrace".

From your own research, discuss the ways in which street or place names reflect the linguistic inheritance of Scots. In your opinion, should we continue to use Scots in street or place names?

24. Describe the characteristics of Scots as used in **one or more than one** specialised field, and account for its survival.

You might consider the uses of Scots in Place and/or Street names, Agriculture, Fishing, the Church, the Law, the Building Trade or any other area that you have studied.

[Turn over

Section 3—Textual Analysis

You must answer **one question only** in this section.

1. Prose fiction [*Pages twenty-four to twenty-seven*]

The following short story ***A Horizon of Obelisks*** *is by the Scottish writer Dorothy K Haynes.*

Read the short story carefully and then answer the question that follows it (*Page twenty-seven*).

A HORIZON OF OBELISKS

They opened the grave in the evening, digging deep, beyond the grass roots, and the roots of small things tangled in the mould like hairs.

The man in the grave felt the chill just before dawn. Soil pattered, rotten wood cracked, and he shrank as the air pressed on him. "Cold," he thought, "right through 5 to my bones," and he moved the bones, disconnected now, under the flesh he thought was there. "Cold," he thought. His arms folded, hugging himself, and there was a wetness of dew, and a weakness over him. He remembered the weakness, and the light going down low, and a queer pinpoint of it lingering on after they had washed and bound him and knelt by his side. Now the light was growing again, and he scrabbled 10 up and lay on the ground like a newly hatched bird, waiting for the day to dry him out.

The sun came up like polished copper, and the angel on the mortuary dome preened its wings and curved them like pincers. Weakly, the man went down the paths, left and right, looking for the way out. It seemed to take a long time. What he remembered about the graveyard went back to his childhood, hot days among the tombstones and 15 daisies, and his mother watching him, smiling on the grass beside a cypress tree. He had always enjoyed going to the graveyard. Heaven, he had thought, would be just like this, smooth grass, bright beds of flowers, and a horizon of obelisks and angels. Perhaps this *was* Heaven . . . ?

He accepted the fact that he had died, remembering how life had narrowed to a 20 needlepoint and gone. But what, then, of the Resurrection? He had always pictured it as a great flapping of wings and an uprush of souls, all crying together and vanishing into the sun, but there had been no trumpets splitting the air, nothing ascending from the green mounds. The angel on the mortuary was rigid against the sailing sky, and he himself had nothing about him that was celestial. In his mind he was as he had once 25 been, a raw, red man in working clothes with a fuzz of ginger over his baldness. He passed his hand over his eyes, and looked about him distractedly. All through the chill of his waking he had heard a bleating and lowing and the flustered clucking of hens, and he remembered how it had once been a comfort to him to know that, when he died, he would lie within sound of the cattle market. That was where he had worked; but 30 how long ago, he could not remember.

Here now was the way out, a little arch let into the grey wall. He looked over his shoulder, as if to ask permission, but no-one stopped him as he laid his hand on the latch, and there was no fiery sword to bleed and burn through him. He stepped out on to the pink grush, and weakly, meekly, made his way past the grave-digger's lodge to 35 the blue tar of the roadway.

It was early yet, the sun level along the streets, and he went with the determined plod of a child making for home. The school playground was a wash of sunlight, and all the pointed windows stood open. By ten o'clock the place would echo like a church with the plainsong of the multiplication tables, but now there was only the janitor, whistling 40 in his peaked cap and boiler suit.

Downhill, where the road narrowed, the butcher was dressing his floor. He walked backwards, blue and white, like a sailor on the golden sawdust, and the man paused, idle and interested; but there was an uneasiness, too, in the death around him, the great bull swinging in chains, the sheep's heads, the bones pink on their ashets—he did not 45 know whether it was kinship or pity. Quickly, he backed out of the shadowed street to where the sunlight sliced the pavement.

What was the time? The clock blazed gold, and the weather vane was as small as a golden bee. It was so high that he had to lean back, his eyes screwing up and up the weathered stone, pasts the frets of the belfry and the white scuds of bird lime. Half 50 past seven. The clouds raced and dizzied him, and his eyes darkened and dropped to the ground. The street was bare, the whole proud sweep of it smiling and empty, but the birds were busy, brown sparrows and slate-coloured doves feeding and fluttering together.

The man went down among the shabby houses behind the church. He was holding 55 himself in as a hurt child holds itself till it reaches home. Down here the pavements were scrabbled with yesterday's games, and the doorsteps dipped in the middle. He paused in a close, and listened in brown shadow. Away up the stairs he heard his own door slam, and he knew that a white flake had fallen from the gas mantle. Every crack in the plaster was familiar, the dusty windows on the landings, the gas pipes branching 60 from the wall. When his mother came to the door he would cling to her and let himself go, put his head on her lap and clutch her skirt and sob and sob and stay with her for ever . . .

The knocker was a grinning brass cat with a bow on its neck, but he poked, two-fingered, at the letterbox. Nobody answered. He knocked harder, listening for a 65 footstep inside, and then he turned away. He did not want to disturb the neighbours, to have them coming out in their dustcaps and aprons, rubbing at the doorknobs as they spied. Down the stairs again, he searched in the yard, in the wash house, among the house-proud scorings of pipe-clay. She might be filling the coal bucket, or emptying the ashes, or shaking the rugs. She was so clear in his mind that he could 70 almost touch her; but she was not there, and he went away with the love in him taut and swollen.

He hung about, hoping to meet her in the streets. The shops put their shades out, and he wandered up and down, remembering this kind of day, the bright joy of it, long ago. No-one spoke to him, and he did not look at faces. The things he added to the 75 turmoil of his mind were little pleasures his mother had shown him, secret things, the amber glass of a door handle, a fluted light in a fruit shop, an alley where the cobbles were sea-rounded and smooth; but he was at a loose end, like a child playing truant . . .

[Turn over

Playing truant . . . from what? He would not think about it. The school emptied, the streets filled with yells and running feet. Every cafe in the town was bursting full, 80 steaming with beef and broth and custard; and then it was afternoon. The clock on the station kept at its eternal semaphore, the signals shifted, the trains fussed and sighed; and past the station wall and the horse trough went the orphan children, four deep, with a Sister of Mercy behind them. Her boots kicked up the hem of her long blue skirt, and her white flyaway hat was like an arum lily. The man wanted to speak to her, 85 because nuns were good women who would help anyone who asked, but he could not explain what troubled him. Time eluded him, like the memory of what had come after this repeated present. He could not think beyond this day, with the dust blowing, and the farmers jostling in the streets, and the brown droves of cattle going by with lowered horns and a yapping at their heels. He did not know what was going to happen next, 90 but when it did happen, it was as if someone had jogged his memory. On a day like this, his mother had taken him into an icecream shop, and in the cool dark they had supped from little glass dishes. Outside, a beggar had squeezed his accordion, with a dirty capful of pennies in the gutter—and there was the beggar, his grey head frowsy, his hands grained with dirt. "*No,*" his mother had said, as he tugged at her sleeve, 95 "*No, he'll just drink it,*" and she had dragged him away from the sighing music and the man's turned up eyes.

The orphan children had gone now, through the chapel gates, and the man stood, lost for a moment, by the dusty horse trough. The roadway filled with a carpet of fawn fleeces, and a car crawled behind them, another and another car, all black. Rigidly, the 100 man stood, watching the funeral. This had happened too, a long time ago. He and his mother would stand on the edge of the pavement, not staring, but taking it all in, the long coffin in the glass hearse, the rainbow wreaths, and the stuffed-looking mourners, not looking out of the window in case they should enjoy the ride. He had had to take off his cap . . . stiffly, he put his hand up, but the cars had passed, round the corner by 105 the market.

He could not follow them. His mother had never intruded when a funeral was on, but later, when it was all over, they would tiptoe in, and look at the wreaths, and read the black-edged cards among the petals. Vaguely, with a sense of filling in time, he made his way to the market. Soon the selling would be over, the rings silent, the pens 110 empty, and children would run round in the empty space gathering feathers and handfuls of white down.

The afternoon was ebbing away in lessening enchantment. A lone cow filled the barns with its bellowing, and men with stiff brooms were sweeping the cobbles. These were none of the men he knew, and they did not pass the time of day. The day was 115 nearly over for them, and all they wanted was to finish and go home for tea.

Timidly, he rubbed a hand over his face. The day, this peculiar day, was ending for him as well. The workers would go to their separate homes, wash at the running tap, and sit down at the table with a woman to wait on them; but he could not go back to that. He was still living out his childhood, the past condensed into a few bright hours, 120 and the hours' slow saddening towards evening. The house would grow dark, the teaplates sour with beetroot and vinegar, the kettle whining as the fire died. And after he had washed, and climbed into the recess bed, listening to his father clearing his throat and knocking out his pipe, the curfew bell would ring, knell, knell, knell, and he would want to sob, thinking of all the evening hymns.

125 "Change and decay in all around I see . . . ." But he would hold back his weeping because his mother would be tired by that time, and she might not have patience with him . . .

Weary, a little bewildered, he turned away from the dunged cobbles and the mournful lowing. Opposite were the main gates of the cemetery, wrought-iron gold-
130 embossed, with a humble little door at the side for those who entered on foot; and through this door went the man, shutting it after him as his mother had taught him when he was a child.

This, he had thought, must be like entering Heaven; but surely Heaven was never meant to be so lonely? There had been no joy in his day, nothing but a yearning and an
135 ache in the heart. If this was Heaven, his mother would come now, surely, in the cool of the evening, walking reverently past the grave, poking among the flowers with stiff gloved fingers . . .

He knelt to look at the cards, but his eyes were blurred, and it was a long time before he realised that she was buried there, and that hers was the funeral he had seen
140 in the wake of the jogging sheep. There was no sorrow in knowing that she was dead. She would sleep as he had done, under the roots and the small pebbles, but if God was willing she would not wake till the Resurrection. He prayed that she would not waken. He himself had been meant to sleep on, but the early cold had roused him.

He sat on an iron bench marked FOR THE USE OF THE PUBLIC, and his arms
145 folded, hugging himself. The ache inside him had eased a little with understanding. At least there would be no more searching; and maybe tomorrow, or one of the grey or golden tomorrows in store, the trumpet would sound, the graves would open, and eternity would begin, —or end.

He sat for a long time, telling himself that there was nothing to be afraid of. The
150 lone cow mourned in the market, and far away, a train trailed its own scream after it. The angel on the mortuary dome flapped its wings against the green sky, and then huddled down to sleep, but the man on the bench could not sleep for the chill. "Cold," he thought. "Right through to my bones . . . ."

Question

Write a critical evaluation of this short story in which you give particular attention to:

- the structure of the narrative
- the relationship established between the "man" and his mother
- the evocation of time and place
- the role of the supernatural in the story.

[Turn over

2. Prose non-fiction [*Pages twenty-eight to thirty-two*]

The Scottish parliament building, which was designed by the late Catalan architect, Enric Miralles, was opened on 9 October 2004. The following article, by Neal Ascherson, was published in ***The Herald Magazine*** *on 28 August 2004.*

Read the extract carefully and then answer the question that follows it (*Page thirty-two*).

They are lucky, those MSPs. When they finally lug their briefcases into the Scottish Parliament, they will be enfolded by a place which turns out to be many places. There are chambers and galleries which sing with genius, and there are secret hiding places which whistle distracting airs. There are dark jungles of dangling light fittings and
5 pipes, and dazzling pools of light in which no lines are straight. You traverse dim, low-ceilinged recesses like Palaeolithic caverns. Then come overwhelming moments as the landscape leaps into the building—cloud shadows sail across Salisbury Craigs and across the carpet in front of the Presiding Officer's desk.

This is a parliament? At first, that seems unlikely. This is the most marvellous and
10 imaginative public structure to rise in Europe for a decade, certainly. But can it be tamed into supporting plenary debates, committee sessions, routine constituency e-mails? I think it can. Not only that, it will be better at the job than a conventional design.

After all, the late, unpredictable Enric Miralles never meant this to be one building.
15 He invented Scotland's parliament as a "dense urban fabric", imitating the sort of built jumble which coagulates organically over centuries. A monastery, for instance. Or a campus. Or a close-packed Fife fishing village.

And with this idea, Miralles—a man whose lightning impulses were often his wisest—somehow also grasped the way that parliaments have changed. Once we
20 imagined a parliament as essentially a single chamber in which one frock-coated orator mounted the tribune and held forth, his views cheered or booed by a rapt audience. But a real-world parliament today is a republic—or campus—of different functions which happen in different places at the same time.

Those old-time plenary meetings matter far less than they once did. The work of
25 elected members is now in fringe gatherings, press briefings, party group meetings, and, above all, committee sessions and hearings where politicians converse rather than orate, cross-question rather than challenge, cooperate rather than confront. This is exactly the way the Scottish Parliament was imagined in the 1990s, when its planners worked out the procedures for a modern democracy. And the huddle of contrasting
30 places at Holyrood—high or low, grand or humble, sombre or witty—is just right for that democratic model.

Miralles, from time to time, changed the images for what he was after. He once talked about upturned boats, a notion which stuck with the media and the public. But he also spoke about a bundle of tree twigs ending in a fan of green leaves. One legend
35 tells that he took such a bunch of leaves to a meeting and threw it on the table: "This is what I have in mind!" Looking at the almost-complete complex, the leaf simile makes more sense. The stems will converge as long green banks, covering the scar where garages are being excavated. The leaves, big and small, are the roofs of lobbies and committee rooms and restaurants. Even the main debating chamber, seen from
40 outside, has vegetable curls and ribs. Maybe this is why the parliament rhymes so effortlessly well with the huge russet and green hill above it.

Here again, Miralles got something deeply right. He set his structures at the landscape, not the townscape. This was probably vanity at one level; I would guess that the closeness of so much fine old masonry irritated Miralles. He looked at the 45 creative opportunities offered by a world-famous street with a palace at one end and a castle at the other, and was bored by them. But Miralles also sensed that Scotland's past is not about streets but about stone and geology and how they have governed human settlement. The MSPs have to look at the hard, handsome rocks which gave Scotland grudging birth, and so they should.

50 The big things about Holyrood are right. Some of the smaller things are not, and they raise political questions as well as aesthetic ones. Scotland's wisest judge of architecture, Professor Isi Metzstein, wrote the other day that Holyrood was over designed: "Every bit of the building is equally elaborate; there is . . . no way to recognise when you have come to something important."

55 There is a political point here too. The MSPs need to be able to hear themselves think. That means not being shouted down at every level by the architect, even if he was a genius. The Miralles voice is very moving when it's at the macro level, in the planetarium space of the debating chamber or in the swirling high spirits of the garden lobby. It's cheerfully audible in the six committee rooms, each one a different irregular 60 shape. But when it comes to the highly designed furniture and fittings, it's as if a penetrating Catalan voice is constantly interrupting: "This is what I have in mind, and this is what I like!"

Take the debating chamber chairs, draped with metal rods and divided into two wooden lobes, like pantaloons designed for the Ballets Russes: they are distracting. 65 The human silhouettes stuck on the chamber walls, apparently to suggest that the public are watching and vigilant, are unfunny.

Personally, I like the little Miralles chair for meditation perched up against the window of each MSP's office, but others find it intrusive. The elected member for Tillietudlum doesn't want to be told to meditate, and neither do they want to be 70 unhealthily fascinated by chair designs or spooky symbols glued to the public gallery. At a certain point, in other words, the architect of a democratic parliament has to pull back and shut up.

Any parliament building which is more than a shed makes a statement of some kind. The task of the elected members, as they tumble in at the start of a 75 parliamentary session, is to size up what the architecture is talking about and then, if necessary, shout it down.

Too many parliaments, in Europe especially, make pompous statements about power rather than democracy. Maybe there is a rule here about styles and messages. Neo-classical parliaments usually have lavish Corinthian capitals on their columns. 80 This is because, consciously or unconsciously, they are built to resemble banks, and their statement is about strongrooms of power secure from greedy democratic fingers. Neo-gothic parliaments, such as Westminster or the gaudy palace on the Danube which is Hungary's parliament, make a different statement, which is about the majesty of history and heritage. This is because they were built by aristocrats, in times when the 85 political classes in Britain and Hungary were mostly landowners.

[Turn over

Shouting down the architecture can be hard. In the Weimar Republic, after the German Empire had been overthrown in 1918, the deputies had to meet in the Reichstag building in Berlin, built a generation earlier at the height of imperial boastfulness. They tried to disinfect it with the spirit of republicanism and social
90 democracy, but the place was too strong.

The novelist Joseph Roth went there in 1924 to cover the opening of a new session, and was shocked. "One could be forgiven for assuming that the magnificent façade with the six great Corinthian pillars is there to greet the representatives of the German people, a little pompously perhaps, but with dignity. But this front entrance isn't. The
95 great doors are kept locked . . . the façade is only for show. The front part of the Reichstag gives the impression of a vast mansion whose owner is away." Instead, the deputies crept in through a side entrance, past scowling busts of German emperors.

Roth saw "majestic overload wherever you look; reheated tradition without innovation, show without warmth, frozen displays of pomp. How should humanity,
100 understanding, compassion exist here? In the 'dome room' there is a chandelier that weighs eight metric tons—as heavy as the fate of the people who own the chandelier."

Roth sensed that democrats who were too frightened to get their own front door opened would not make great defenders of democracy. He was right. The architecture won when Hitler came to power a few years later.

105 The Reichstag was burned out in 1933, and its shell was stormed by Soviet troops in 1945. Today, reconstructed as the Bundestag of a reunited Germany, it tells a different story of hope and confidence with big contemporary paintings, Norman Foster's wonderful glass cupola, and the graffiti scratched by Russian soldiers carefully preserved.

110 The Bundestag members control their building now. It wasn't so when the first West German deputies sat in a soulless converted training college at Bonn. They were as timid as their Weimar ancestors. The fat bully who had the concession for the overpriced Bundestag restaurant demanded that all other food outlets within a mile radius be shut down. When the deputies objected, he threatened them: "Ignorant
115 provincial nobodies, who haven't yet learned democratic behaviour." Terrified, they caved in. It was years before they found the courage to sack him.

Sometimes, a parliament's architecture can be a silent reproach. In the Communist era, I came to know the Sejm, the Polish parliament in Warsaw. Its architecture was a modernist version of Greek classical, very white and pure with gleaming marble
120 columns which bulged and tapered in a very un-Greek way.

Here a tame parliament met to have imitation debates. But the deputies were embarrassed by their elegant surroundings which spoke to them, irrepressibly, of the times in which they were designed—times when a free and newly independent nation was imagining its own future. The ministers sat uncomfortably crammed into a set of
125 pews under the speaker's dais. They resembled passengers on a circus death ride, or (the image preferred by the contemptuous Polish public) prisoners in the dock at a fraud trial. Something about the Sejm chamber always rendered the powerful faintly ridiculous.

So what is the right architecture for a democracy? I remember a legislature in
130 Uganda, the building at Mmengo in Kampala which is called the Great Lukiiko. This was the parliament of the kingdom of Buganda. Its form was simple: a huge thatched hall made of clay, its walls several yards thick.

Today, after many upheavals and closures, the Lukiiko building is again in use as a parliament. It would be pushing it to describe the Lukiiko as a democratic assembly, at
135 least in my time. Uganda then was still a British protectorate. In the hall sat the Gombolola and Saza chiefs in white gowns. Facing them on his throne was the Kabaka of Buganda in his embroidered robe, while beside him on a slightly lower throne the governor sweated in full uniform with epaulettes, cocked hat and plumes. And if the chiefs looked over their shoulders, they could see another important figure. This was
140 the royal strangler in his saffron-coloured robe, leaning against the jamb of the open front door and lightly tapping a knotted loop of cord against his leg.

But the point of the Lukiiko was its windows. They were enormous, deep embrasures, left open and unglazed. And at each window stood a crowd of ordinary people, squeezing into the openings and sitting on the broad sills. They were allowed
145 to listen, but they were also allowed to interrupt, to shout comments, to suggest what should be debated. I don't remember much notice being taken of them, but their right to be part of the Lukiiko, the tradition that decisions taken without the presence of the listening people were invalid, seemed absolute. And in the architecture of the Great Lukiiko their right was given solid form.

150 And so to Westminster. Charles Barry designed the Palace of Westminster after its destruction by fire in 1834, and Augustus Pugin did the decoration. The Lords and Commons chambers are monuments to adversarial politics, with their rectangular plan of benches divided into two hostile, mutually confronting tiers. In that sense the architecture is brilliantly appropriate, perpetuating all that is worst about the dog-
155 bites-dog traditions of British politics.

But the layout and decoration left by Barry and Pugin also make the palace a huge fossil of Victorian values, above all, hierarchy and history. Each rank and class has its own carefully graded privileges, in terms of space and access. There is an MPs' entrance, a peers' entrance, a public entrance and of course a sovereign's entrance.
160 Along the warrens of segregated corridors, locked doors conceal gorgeous or gaudy rooms done in neo-gothic style by Pugin, each allotted to a social grade or class up to the sovereign's magnificent Robing Room with its Arthurian frescos, the Princesses' Chamber and so on.

The furnishings and décor of the House of Commons speak of heritage, tradition
165 and continuity. But where in this gothic warren is democracy at home? Or openness, or equality, or even accountability? All these are principles which can be expressed in architecture, space and materials. The new building at Holyrood expresses many of them, very deliberately. But the Palace of Westminster was not built to house them.

Compared to some of these examples, Holyrood's architecture guides MSPs
170 towards the principles laid down for Scotland's democracy: openness, accountability, equality and informality. It's true that it is not at all a Presbyterian building. Those principles are not expressed at Holyrood through the Scottish tradition of an austere, undecorated meeting hall. Neither is it a modernist structure, in which "transparency" is symbolised very literally by glass curtain walls and bare concourses without a
175 shadow to hide behind. This is a European inspiration, an introverted warren of corridors and contrasts.

[Turn over

Openness in this parliament is not so much in the design as in the rules. There is almost no place in the entire complex which a member of the public cannot reach, if not by simply walking in, then by the invitation of an MSP.

180 The best current comment on the new Holyrood is that it challenges the devolved parliament to "raise its game". This is a strong-willed masterpiece of architecture, and the MSPs will have to grow bigger to dominate it.

At first sight, Holyrood is intimidating. Miralles said of it: "This is a great game with time." He was referring to the game his buildings play with the geology outside, 185 but the MSPs may feel initially that they are merely pawns in a superb but mystifying game played by a craftsman from beyond the grave.

That awe they must overcome. This place which is many places is not there to be revered. It is meant to ring with voices, to be tramped through, to be taken for granted, even to be changed and modified when its occupants feel like it. The bigger 190 the politics undertaken here, the sooner democracy will be master in its own house.

Question

"So what is the right architecture for a democracy?" (line 129)

How effectively does Neal Ascherson explore the issues raised by this question in the course of his article?

In your answer, you should make detailed reference to his use of language, imagery, structure, comparison and contrast, and any other feature of his writing you think significant.

[Turn over for 3. Poetry *Pages thirty-four to thirty-five*]

3. Poetry [*Pages thirty-four to thirty-five*]

*Read carefully the poem **Jugged Hare** by Jean Earle and then answer the questions (a), (b) and (c) that follow it (Page thirty-five). Jugged Hare is a dish in which the hare, after preparation, is cooked in a closed earthenware vessel.*

JUGGED HARE

She mourned the long-ears
Hung in the pantry, his shot fur
Softly dishevelled. She smoothed that,
Before gutting—yet she would rather
5 Sicken herself, than cheat my father
Of his jugged hare.

A tender lady, freakish as the creature—
But resolute. She peeled it to its tail.
Oh, fortitude! Her rings sparked in and out
10 Of newspaper wipes. Blood in a bowl,
Sacrificial gravy. A rarely afforded
Bottle of port.

She sustained marriage
On high events, as a child plays house.
15 Dramas, conciliations—
Today, the hare. She sent me out
To bury the skin,
Tossed the heart to the cat.

She was in full spate.

20 Fragrance of wine and herbs
Blessed our kitchen; like the hare's dessert
Of wild thyme; or like his thighs
As though braised by God. She smiled
And dished up on willow,
25 Having a nice touch in framing
One-off scenarios.

After the feast, my father was a lover
Deeply enhanced.
I heard them go to bed,
30 Kissing—still inside her picture.
Later, I heard her sob
And guessed it was the hare

Troubled her. My father slept,
Stunned with tribute. She lay now
35 Outside her frame, in the hare's dark

Hating her marital skills
And her lady-hands, that could flense a hare
Because she wooed a man.
In years to come,
40 I understood.

Questions

(*a*) Make a detailed analysis of the means by which the poet gives significance to the hare in lines 1–12.

(*b*) Discuss the ways in which, in lines 13–38, the poet explores the nature of the marriage presented in this poem.

(*c*) What is it, in your opinion, that the speaker in the poem eventually "understood"?

[Turn over

4. Drama [*Pages thirty-six to forty-three*]

Rona Munro's play **Iron** *(2002) takes place in a women's prison. The central characters are Fay and Josie, a mother and daughter who have had no contact since Fay's arrest and conviction for the murder of her husband, Josie's father, fifteen years earlier when Josie was ten.*

The play begins as Josie tries to visit her mother and Fay agrees to allow the visit.

The extract which follows is from the third scene of Act One. Josie and Fay are meeting for the first time in 15 years. The meeting takes place in the visiting room of the prison. There is a great buzz of conversation around them.

The characters in the extract are:

JOSIE	*Fay's daughter aged 25*
FAY	*Josie's mother aged 45*
TWO GUARDS	*One male and one female.*

Read the extract carefully and then answer the question that follows it (Page forty-three).

IRON

	JOSIE:	[*looking round*]. This isn't too bad is it?
	FAY:	What isn't?
	JOSIE:	This place.
	FAY:	You think so do you?
5	JOSIE:	Well, I mean . . . there's flowers out there.
	FAY:	Eh?
	JOSIE:	Acres of them. Trees. Grass.
	FAY:	And do you see me skipping across it with a picnic basket? Oh they make it look good.
10	JOSIE:	No it's just not what I expected.
	FAY:	What did you expect?
	JOSIE:	Barbed wire, Rottweilers. I didn't expect geraniums.
		[*Pause.*]
	FAY:	It's not what you think. It's not a hotel.
15	JOSIE:	I was joking. I'm sorry.
	FAY:	It's no joke.
	JOSIE:	Just more cheerful than I thought.
	FAY:	[*upset*]. Well. There you go.
	JOSIE:	Well . . . that's good isn't it?
20	FAY:	What?
	JOSIE:	That you're not all locked up in iron bars and concrete.

FAY: I could see how you'd think that.

[*Pause.*]

This is a long time to sit without a fag. What time is it?

25 JOSIE *shows her watch.* FAY *reaches out to it.*

Oh that's beautiful. Haven't you got beautiful things?

JOSIE: [*still offering it*]. Here. Try it on.

FAY *looks at the* GUARDS, *shaking her head.*

FAY: We're not allowed to touch.

30 JOSIE *looks at* GUARD 2. GUARD 2 *is watching them. She smiles.*

JOSIE: They won't mind. I've talked to that one. She's O.K.

FAY: We're not allowed.

JOSIE: Really?

35 FAY: [*leaning back, hands ostentatiously held up and empty*]. Stop it. You'll get me into trouble.

JOSIE *leans back.*

JOSIE: I'm not doing this very well am I?

FAY: Doing what?

40 JOSIE: I just don't know how to get into it.

FAY: Oh you don't want to get into anything. So. Your Gran's dead?

JOSIE: Yes.

FAY: Was she bad, at the end?

JOSIE: She wasn't herself.

45 FAY: She used to love me. She said I was the daughter she never had. Suppose that was you in the end . . .

A pause. FAY *is trembling.*

She never visited me. She never came near me. I don't know what she told you . . . What she must have told you about me . . . and your
50 Dad . . . Oh this is no good, this is no good . . . [*She's shaking, on the verge of tears.*] Look I'm getting all upset. I want to go back. I want to go back to my room. I want to go.

FAY *starts to get up.*

JOSIE: Shhhh, no, don't please, don't go . . .

55 *Reluctantly* FAY *sits again. She takes a few deep breaths, getting herself under control.*

FAY: Look. This isn't how you do things. You need to learn how to behave . . .

	JOSIE:	I'm sorry.
60	FAY:	It's not the zoo you know, you can't come in when the fancy takes you and throw me a bun! Give me a bit of small talk at least tell me about the weather or . . . Christ I canny take this in . . .
		Pause. JOSIE *sits, tense.* FAY *won't look at her.*
	JOSIE:	I'm sorry. Maybe we'll do this another time.
65		FAY *instantly changes.*
	FAY:	Oh no oh don't, no don't, don't go. I haven't seen you in such a long . . . such a long time. [*Starts to cry.*] My wee girl. My wee girl . . .
70		JOSIE *watches as* FAY *snuffles, groping in her sleeve for a hanky she hasn't got. She wipes her face with her hands.*
	JOSIE:	It's sunny. The weather's warm.
	FAY:	I can see that.
	JOSIE:	I shouldn't have upset you.
	FAY:	It's fine. I'm fine.
75	JOSIE:	I wanted to ask you . . .
	FAY:	No! Just wait will you.
		I don't like to get upset. There's nowhere to go with it.
	JOSIE:	No.
80	FAY:	I need to settle myself. This is no good. No good at all. Tell me something.
	JOSIE:	What?
	FAY:	What did you have for breakfast?
	JOSIE:	Sorry?
	FAY:	Tell me. Please. Just keep talking to me.
85	JOSIE:	Toast.
	FAY:	Hot?
	JOSIE:	Aye.
	FAY:	Butter?
	JOSIE:	Olive spread.
90	FAY:	What's that?
	JOSIE:	It's an olive oil spread.
	FAY:	Is it like butter?
	JOSIE:	It's better for you.
	FAY:	Is that like a slimming thing.
95	JOSIE:	I suppose.

FAY: [*quickly, before she can panic again*]. Tell me something else.

JOSIE: Did Dad brush his teeth in the kitchen sink?

FAY: What?

JOSIE: I've got a very clear memory of that, Dad brushing his teeth in the
100 kitchen sink when it was still full of dirty pans and plates. And you shouted at him, and he looked at you with his mouth full of foam. And he looked like a dog you'd caught with its nose in a biscuit tin.

FAY: That's dirty.

JOSIE: Did he do that? Is that the sort of thing he'd do?

105 FAY: How would I know now?

Pause.

JOSIE: Mum never talked about him. It made her cry.

FAY: Your Gran?

JOSIE: Yes.

110 FAY: You called her Mum?

JOSIE: . . . Yes.

FAY: That would've killed me if I'd thought about it.

JOSIE: I'm . . . sorry.

FAY: It's alright. She's dead now.

115 JOSIE: Yes.

FAY: Can't speak ill of the dead.

Pause.

Your Dad would have been glad to see how you turned out.

JOSIE: Would he?

120 FAY: Tell the truth he'd've rather you were a rock star. He wanted to be a rock star. Bugger was tone deaf but he loved his guitar. Punk. Punk was his big chance. Tone deaf was an asset for punk wasn't it?

JOSIE: I don't know really.

FAY: Course you don't. You don't remember back then. What am I
125 thinking of?

JOSIE: What . . . ? [*Suddenly she can't speak.*]

FAY: Yes?

JOSIE *shakes her head.*

Go on. You were going to ask me something?

130 JOSIE: What did he look like?

FAY: Your Dad? Oh he was a looker. I thought he was a looker, had a bit of a gut on him but he was gorgeous. Didn't your Gran have photos?

	JOSIE:	Yes . . . but only when he was younger . . . before . . .
	FAY:	You're upset aren't you? Don't go getting upset. It's alright.
135	JOSIE:	Is it O.K? Are you O.K? You don't mind talking about him?
	FAY:	No. I don't mind. Did you think I would?
	JOSIE:	You just said . . . I don't want to upset you again.
	FAY:	I often think about your Dad.
	JOSIE:	Do you?
140	FAY:	I miss him. I miss him yet.
	JOSIE:	[*quiet*] Do you?
	FAY:	Yes. [*Looking at* JOSIE.] Oh now I know you. Now I can see you. You look about ten years old. Don't sweetie. Don't upset yourself.
	JOSIE:	I'm fine.
145	FAY:	Course you are.
	JOSIE:	I'm fine. Really.
	FAY:	I remember every moment of your life from when you were born till the day they took me away from you. I remember what you looked like, what you wore, how your hair was, what you said . . . what you
150		felt.
	JOSIE:	Have you got photographs?
	FAY:	No. I haven't got anything.
	JOSIE:	Wouldn't they let you bring them?
	FAY:	She wouldn't let me. She kept everything.
155	JOSIE:	I never saw them.
	FAY:	She probably burnt them. She probably hated me.
		Pause.
		Didn't she?
	JOSIE:	I don't know.
160	FAY:	She was his mother.
		We used to go out every Friday night. Just her and me.
	JOSIE:	What did you do?
	FAY:	We'd have three drinks in the White Rose then we'd have an Italian at Donatello's . . . I loved Donatello's, is it still there? Corner of the
165		High Street?
	JOSIE:	I don't know. We moved.
	FAY:	Course you did. I couldn't find you. I didn't know where you were.
	JOSIE:	You looked for me?
	FAY:	I asked. They wouldn't tell me where you were.

170 JOSIE: But that's . . . they shouldn't do that should they?

FAY: It doesn't matter. You found me.

JOSIE: That's terrible . . .

FAY: Oh that's the least of it.

JOSIE: But we should complain!

175 FAY: I don't like thinking about it. I don't like upsetting myself. I'd rather remember the good times, Donatello's and your Nan all done up with green eyeshadow and you still sitting up when I got in, asleep on your Dad's lap in front of the fire.

JOSIE *catches her breath.*

180 Remember?

JOSIE: No . . . I . . .

FAY: Tell me about yourself.

JOSIE: I don't know . . .

FAY: You're pretty. You've got lovely clothes, a bit of money. You've had

185 your heart broken once at least . . .

JOSIE: Not really I . . .

FAY: Well you're divorced, whatever . . . no steady love now, jetting round the world . . .

JOSIE: No.

190 FAY: No? You're better than television. I haven't experienced anything past the eight o'clock watershed for fifteen years. No sex, no drugs, no rock and roll . . . I'm getting light headed just looking at you. How's your social life? What clubs do you go to? What's the last place you had a drink that wasn't in Britain?

195 JOSIE: San Diego.

FAY: There you go. Where's that then?

JOSIE: California.

FAY: California. With the oranges and the sunshine. What did you have?

JOSIE: God . . . I can't remember that.

200 FAY: Try. Go on. Tell me.

JOSIE: I don't know . . . a beer? Maybe a margherita.

FAY: That sounds like the business. That's with tequila?

JOSIE: Yes.

FAY: That's a mad drink, tequila.

205 JOSIE: Yes.

FAY: [*laughing*]. Isn't it? What was the place like? What's San Diego like?

JOSIE: It's . . . It's a huge city. Glass and metal skyscrapers and it's got a zoo . . .

FAY: Oh lovely. Lions and tigers and bears?

210 JOSIE: [*uncertain*]. Eh . . . yeah. And it's got a beach . . . Well it's got about eighty beaches, right in the city. People walk out their houses and onto a surf board.

FAY: California eh? And where were you? Was it a nice hotel?

JOSIE: It was alright.

215 FAY: Were you on expenses?

JOSIE: Yes.

FAY: God, what's that like? Do you empty the mini bar?

JOSIE: You keep your receipts.

FAY: So you were drinking a margherita . . .

220 JOSIE: Yes.

FAY: What was the bar like? Who were you with?

JOSIE: It was . . . I was in the old town. That's up on the hill. It's . . . well it's not really old.

FAY: How d'you mean?

225 JOSIE: It's American old. Anything older than me is an antique you know?

FAY: God you've really been to America haven't you? Tell me.

JOSIE: It's nice.

FAY: Come on darlin', let me see it. What did it look like?

JOSIE: I don't know what you . . . ?

230 FAY: [*interrupts*]. Give me a picture. What did you see?

JOSIE: [*hesitates*]. Little low houses with red and orange walls and roofs, there's trolley buses, that's trams . . . and a view over the bay . . . The air smells of charcoal and barbecue and bushes with flowers the size of hats grow like weeds.

235 FAY: Aw lovely . . .

JOSIE: . . . And I was sitting outside this bar, under a palm roof, watching a mariachi band annoy the tourists at the restaurant next door . . .

FAY: What's that?

JOSIE: Guys in Mexican hats with trumpets.

240 FAY: Right. I knew that.

JOSIE: So I was just, drinking my drink there. With Dave.

FAY: Ah here we go. Who's Dave?

JOSIE: He works in the San Diego office of the company I was with.

FAY: Nice?

245 JOSIE: Gorgeous. Gay.

FAY: Aw bad luck. What did you do? What did you talk about?

JOSIE: This and that. We watched the sunset.

FAY: Lovely.

JOSIE: Watched all the skateboarders going past . . .

250 FAY: See now I've got a picture of you. Now I'm getting an idea who you are. It's like a postcard.

[*END OF EXTRACT*]

Question

Make a detailed analysis of Rona Munro's use of dialogue in this extract and assess its effectiveness in showing Josie and Fay moving towards some understanding of each other.

[Turn over

Section 4—Reading the Media

You must answer **one question only** in this section.

Category A—Film

1. "*Directors think visually; even if you turned off the sound track, anybody could figure out what was going on.*"

With detailed reference to **one** or **more than one** film, discuss the extent to which the director relies on cinematography and mise-en-scène to create meaning.

2. Analyse and evaluate the effectiveness of closure in **two** or **three** films.

Category B—Television

3. "*If it bleeds, it leads.*"

To what extent and in what ways does this guideline appear to have shaped news **or** current affairs **or** documentary programmes you have studied?

4. "*To be effective, television soap opera must always create a credible and dynamic community.*"

Discuss with reference to **one** or **more than one** current soap opera.

Category C—Radio

5. "*Radio is the one medium of information and entertainment which accommodates its audience's varying situations, tastes and attention capacity.*"

Discuss some of the means by which radio "accommodates" its audience. You may wish to refer to such aspects as programme structure, content and scheduling, and to the ways in which radio addresses its audience.

6. With reference to a range of examples, assess the ability of radio to exploit its comic potential as a non-visual medium.

Category D—Print journalism

7. "*News values favour bad news, preferably close to home, with human interest centred on a personality.*"

How far do you agree? Support your answer with detailed reference to **one** newspaper's prioritising and treatment of a particular news story or issue.

NB You may not use the materials provided for Question 8 in order to answer Question 7.

8. The following two front pages are from *The Sun* (*Page forty-six*) and *The Independent* (*Page forty-seven*) of February 18, 2003, each featuring the same syndicated image of David Beckham.

Compare and contrast the treatment of the Beckham story in *The Sun* with its treatment in *The Independent*.

You may wish to consider:

- the images of Beckham—in terms of cropping and framing
- the cultural codes which establish representations of Beckham
- the headlines and written copy, their content and tone, and how they affect the reader's interpretation of the story
- the news values demonstrated in the way the story is prioritised.

[Turn over

THE Sun 20p

Tuesday, February 18, 2003 20p www.thesun.co.uk

MEL C SINKS SPICE REUNION

EXCLUSIVE –PAGE 7

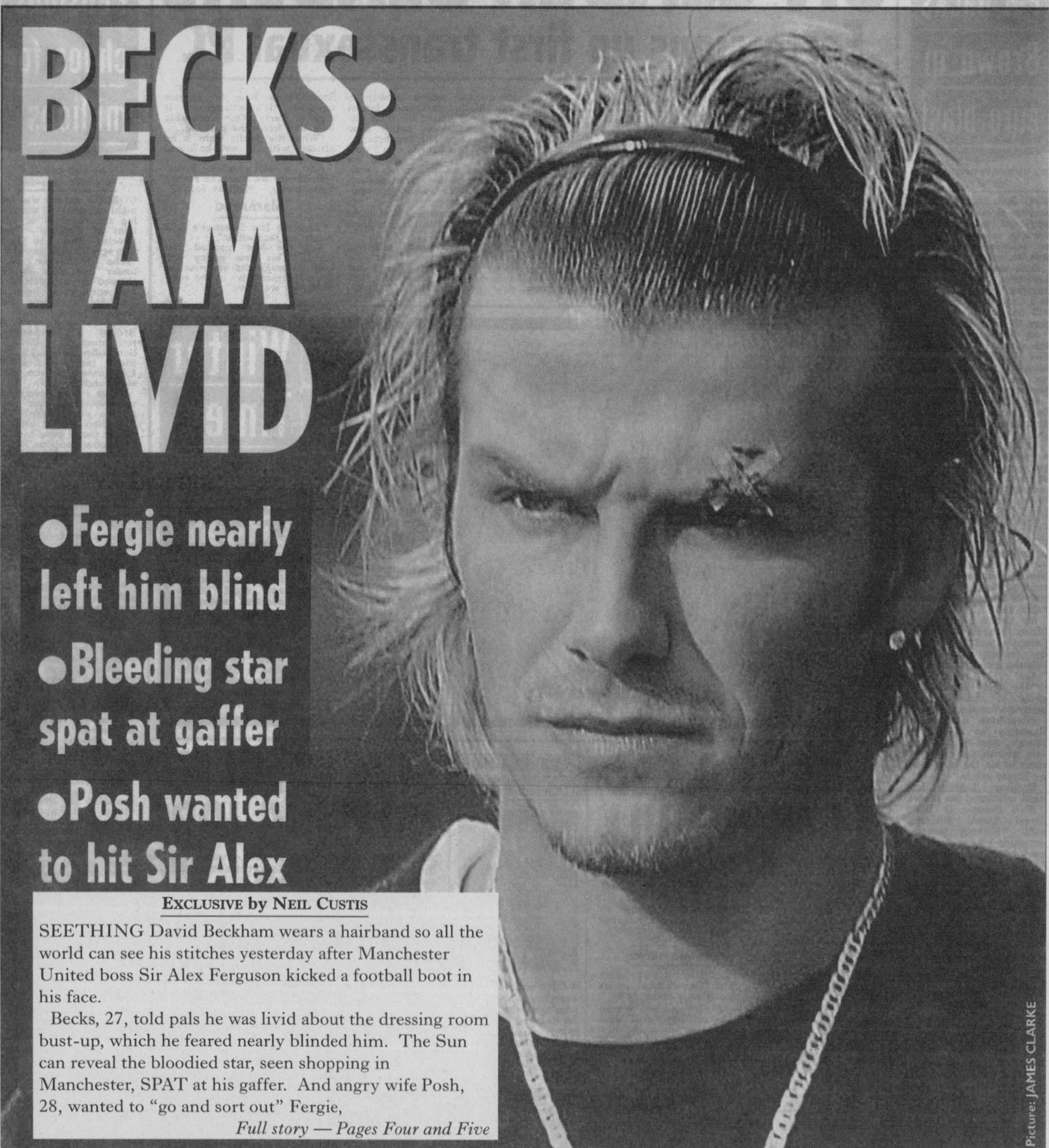

BECKS: I AM LIVID

- Fergie nearly left him blind
- Bleeding star spat at gaffer
- Posh wanted to hit Sir Alex

EXCLUSIVE by NEIL CUSTIS

SEETHING David Beckham wears a hairband so all the world can see his stitches yesterday after Manchester United boss Sir Alex Ferguson kicked a football boot in his face.

Becks, 27, told pals he was livid about the dressing room bust-up, which he feared nearly blinded him. The Sun can reveal the bloodied star, seen shopping in Manchester, SPAT at his gaffer. And angry wife Posh, 28, wanted to "go and sort out" Fergie,

Full story — Pages Four and Five

Picture: JAMES CLARKE

THE INDEPENDENT
THE BROADER VIEW
www.independent.co.uk TUESDAY 18 FEBRUARY 2003 (Republic of Ireland €0.90)

SLOW BUSINESS
The Hours? It seemed more like days to me
PHILIP HENSHER, PAGE 15

WHY I'M KILLING OFF COLD FEET
Mike Bullen, creator of the hit series, on the end of an era MEDIA IN THE REVIEW, PAGES 8-10

NAZI BUSINESS
How the Hitler industry is still making millions
ANALYSIS, PAGE 13

France set to block second UN resolution on Saddam

BY STEPHEN CASTLE IN BRUSSELS AND PAUL WAUGH

TONY BLAIR paved the way last night for possible war against Iraq without the crucial political cover of a second UN resolution, as European divisions on how to tackle Saddam Hussein were sharply exposed at an EU summit.

As Jacques Chirac, the French President, indicated, France would block a second UN resolution authorising war in the near future, the Government gave its clearest warning yet that it could back military conflict without the international blessing that many Britons say they want.

Yesterday's comments could herald the biggest gamble of Mr Blair's premiership. Until now the Prime Minister has said that he would only back military action if it is sanctioned by the UN, or if a second resolution designed to do so were withheld unreasonably.

But following last Friday's neutral presentation by Hans Blix, the chief UN weapons inspector, to the Security Council and the huge demonstrations across the continent at the weekend, Mr Blair is on the defensive and under huge pressure. His moral justification for war appeared to have been further weakened last night after Downing Street conceded that President Saddam could be allowed to remain in power if he disarmed fully.

Arriving for last night's emergency summit in Brussels, M. Chirac, who has led opposition of a rush to war, took the initiative, buoyed by the developments of the last four days. "War is always the worst solution," he said, adding: "That is our position which leads us to conclude it isn't necessary today to have a second resolution."

INSIDE

☛ **THE THREAT OF WAR: Further reports and analysis** THIS SECTION PAGE 2

☛ **Leading article, Donald Macintyre and David Clark** THIS SECTION PAGE 14

One in the eye for Becks: Ferguson admits he put the boot in

David Beckham sports his stitches yesterday, out shopping in Manchester
Eamonn and James Clarke

BY PETER ANTHONY

LAST YEAR it was David Beckham's foot that dominated front pages—now it is his eyebrow. Only this time it was not an over-zealous Argentinian defender that sent the England and Manchester United icon in search of urgent medical treatment but his own manager.

The relationship between Beckham and Sir Alex Ferguson, the high lord of Old Trafford, has always been said to be strained because the stratospheric profile of British football's most famous individual grated with his manager's "team-first" ethos. But on Saturday it was stretched to the limit when Sir Alex, after watching United being knocked out of the FA Cup by Arsenal, stormed into the home dressing room and kicked an errant boot that just happened to hurtle into Beckham's face.

Two stitches were needed on the gashed left eyebrow of the midfielder, who then reportedly stormed out of the ground, 25 minutes before the rest of his team-mates.

Initially, United refused to confirm the tabloid reports of the incident, saying: "Whatever happens in the dressing room remains private."

And then Sir Alex broke the silence by admitting his wayward shot. "It's one of those freak acts of nature. It's over, what a freak, and it'll never happen again," he said.

The pair have fallen out before, including a time when Sir Alex ordered Beckham from the training ground after he missed a practice session to look after his son Brooklyn.

Since that incident, the irascible manager and his gifted protégé were believed to have patched things up between them. However, the only thing being patched up yesterday was Beckham's eyebrow.

**Full report, page 26;
James Lawton, page 22**

Category E—Advertising

9. *"Advertising celebrates consumption and materialism by suggesting that goods can make us happy, successful, desirable and envied."*

   Discuss with reference to a range of advertisements **or** to **one** advertising campaign.

10. Examine carefully the two advertisements, published in *The Times* magazine in the summer of 2003, for San Pellegrino and for Malvern mineral waters respectively.

    NB These advertisements are provided separately as colour inserts.

    How effective are they in establishing a distinctive brand identity for each product?

    You may wish to consider:

    - the use of technical codes—camera (distance, focus, lens), composition, lighting and colour
    - the cultural codes which establish the representation of subject and setting
    - the contrasting stereotypes of national identity and how these are confirmed or subverted
    - how the qualities of the product are incorporated into the narrative of each advertisement
    - the role of the written codes.

[*END OF QUESTION PAPER*]

STILL
malvern
The Original
ENGLISH NATURAL MINERAL WATER
malvern. not quite middle england.
Since 1851
'Malvern' is a registered trademark of Atlantic Industries.

BOTTLED AT THE SOURCE, SAN PELLEGRINO TERME - ITALY
S.PELLEGRINO
SPARKLING NATURAL MINERAL WATER
Prolonged socializing may result.
Whatever language you speak, *live in Italian.*

2006 | Advanced Higher

X115/701

NATIONAL QUALIFICATIONS 2006

FRIDAY, 12 MAY
1.00 PM – 4.00 PM

ENGLISH
ADVANCED HIGHER

There are four sections in this paper.

Depending on the options you have chosen, you must answer **one** or **two** questions.

If you have submitted a Creative Writing folio, you must answer only **one** question.

Otherwise, you must answer **two** questions.

If you are required to answer only **one question**

- it must be taken from **Section 1—Literary Study**
- you must leave the examination room **after 1 hour 30 minutes**.

If you are required to answer **two questions**

- your first must be taken from **Section 1—Literary Study**
- your second must be taken from **a different section**
- each answer must be written in **a separate answer booklet**
- the maximum time allowed for any question is **1 hour 30 minutes**.

You must identify each question you attempt by indicating clearly

- **the title of the section** from which the question has been taken
- **the number of the question** within that section.

You must also write inside the front cover of your Literary Study answer booklet

- **the topic** of your Specialist Study (Dissertation)
- **the texts** used in your Specialist Study (Dissertation).

Section 1—Literary Study

This section is **mandatory** for all candidates.

You must answer **one question only** in this section.

DRAMA

1. Bridie

How far do you agree that the key to the success of Bridie's plays is his careful shaping of dramatic structure?

You should support your answer with evidence from **each** of the specified plays.

2. Byrne

"For all its riotous comedy, ***The Slab Boys Trilogy*** *articulates a passionately serious political vision."*

Discuss.

3. Chekhov

"Central to the dramatic effectiveness of a Chekhov play is not so much action or incident but the changing perceptions and feelings of characters."

How far do you agree?

You may base your answer on *The Cherry Orchard* **or** on *Uncle Vanya* **or** on both plays.

4. Glover

Discuss Glover's dramatic treatment of human loneliness in *The Straw Chair* **and** in *Bondagers*.

5. Lindsay

"Lindsay's shift in focus—from the allegorical figures which dominate Part One to the social types that come to the fore in Part Two—is vital to the successful promotion of his central argument."

Analyse the structure of *Ane Satyre of the Thrie Estaitis* in the light of this assertion.

6. Lochhead

Analyse and evaluate the various ways in which Lochhead uses humour in *Mary Queen of Scots Got Her Head Chopped Off* **and** in *Dracula*.

7. McLellan

Drawing evidence from *Jamie the Saxt* **and** *The Flouers o Edinburgh*, describe and evaluate some of the distinctive features of McLellan's dialogue.

8. Pinter

Discuss the extent to which variations of tone and mood contribute to the dramatic effectiveness of **each** of the specified plays.

9. Shakespeare

(*a*) Make a detailed examination of Shakespeare's dramatic treatment of kingship in *Hamlet* **or** in *King Lear*.

OR

(*b*) Compare and contrast the principal features of Shakespeare's dramatic treatment of kingship in *Hamlet* with the principal features of his dramatic treatment of kingship in *King Lear*.

10. Shaw

"***Major Barbara*** *and* ***St Joan*** *present us with heroines who are models of what Shaw has called 'creative evolution'—ideals of human aspiration and innovation.*"

How far do you agree?

11. Stoppard

"*Dramatic tension in Stoppard's plays arises from the presentation of protagonists confronted by destructive and unpredictable forces.*"

Discuss with reference to *Rosencrantz and Guildenstern are Dead* **and** *Arcadia*.

12. Williams

Discuss Williams's dramatic exploration of the relationship between the "old South" and the "new South" in *The Glass Menagerie* **and** in *A Streetcar Named Desire*.

[Turn over

POETRY

13. Chaucer

"*The interest is not simply in the Tale itself but in the Tale as characteristic of the teller.*"

Discuss with reference to *The Pardoner's Prologue and Tale* and to any **one** other Tale.

14. Coleridge

"*In the poetry of Coleridge, Nature is seen not only as a source of wonder but also as a moral guide and teacher.*"

Discuss.

15. Donne and the metaphysical poets

"*The most notable characteristic of metaphysical poetry is its preoccupation with individual experience, its unabashed concentration upon the self.*"

How far do you agree?

You should support your answer with evidence drawn from the language, imagery and tone of **three** or **four** metaphysical poems.

16. Duffy

"*Duffy's character studies—the affectionate, the gently ironic, the bitingly satirical—always impress with the firmness of the poet's control of tone.*"

Discuss with reference to **three** or **four** poems.

17. Dunbar

Examine Dunbar's poetic treatment of particular aspects of the social life of his day in **two** or **three** poems.

18. Dunn

"*One of the distinguishing features of Dunn's poetry is the sensitivity with which it portrays ordinary people—with all their human weaknesses.*"

Analyse **three** or **four** poems in the light of this assertion.

19. Fergusson

With reference to **two** or **three** poems, analyse some of the principal techniques employed by Fergusson to satirise human folly and corruption.

20. Heaney

The following poem, ***Sunlight****, is the first of two poems dedicated to Mossbawn, Heaney's childhood home, and written for Mary Heaney.*

Read the poem carefully and then answer the questions that follow it.

Mossbawn: Two Poems in Dedication
For Mary Heaney

1 Sunlight

There was a sunlit absence.
The helmeted pump in the yard
heated its iron,
water honeyed

5 in the slung bucket
and the sun stood
like a griddle cooling
against the wall

of each long afternoon.
10 So, her hands scuffled
over the bakeboard,
the reddening stove

sent its plaque of heat
against her where she stood
15 in a floury apron
by the window.

Now she dusts the board
with a goose's wing,
now sits, broad-lapped,
20 with whitened nails

and measling shins:
here is a space
again, the scone rising
to the tick of two clocks.

25 And here is love
like a tinsmith's scoop
sunk past its gleam
in the meal-bin.

(*a*) "And here is love" (line 25). Analyse the means by which Heaney explores aspects of love in this poem.

(*b*) Go on to discuss the means by which he explores aspects of love in **two** or **three** other poems.

[Turn over

21. Hopkins

What do you consider to be the most distinctive features of Hopkins's use of imagery?

Support your answer with evidence drawn from a range of poems.

22. Morgan

The following poem refers to a painting of a Glasgow scene by the Scottish artist, Joan Eardley, which Morgan owned.

Read the poem carefully and then answer the questions that follow it.

TO JOAN EARDLEY

Pale yellow letters
humbly straggling across
the once brilliant red
of a broken shop-face
5 CONFECTIO
and a blur of children
at their games, passing,
gazing as they pass
at the blur of sweets
10 in the dingy, cosy
Rottenrow window—
an Eardley on my wall.
Such rags and streaks
that master us!—
15 that fix what the pick
and bulldozer have crumbled
to a dingier dust,
the living blur
fiercely guarding
20 energy that has vanished,
cries filling still
the unechoing close!
I wandered by the rubble
and the houses left standing
25 kept a chill, dying life
in their islands of stone.
No window opened
as the coal cart rolled
and the coalman's call
30 fell coldly to the ground.
But the shrill children
jump on my wall.

(*a*) Analyse the means by which Morgan explores aspects of Glasgow in this poem.

(*b*) Go on to discuss the means by which he explores aspects of Glasgow in **two** or **three** other poems.

23. Plath

Read the following poem carefully and then answer the questions that follow it.

Morning Song

Love set you going like a fat gold watch.
The midwife slapped your footsoles, and your bald cry
Took its place among the elements.

Our voices echo, magnifying your arrival. New statue.
5 In a drafty museum, your nakedness
Shadows our safety. We stand round blankly as walls.

I'm no more your mother
Than the cloud that distills a mirror to reflect its own slow
Effacement at the wind's hand.

10 All night your moth-breath
Flickers among the flat pink roses. I wake to listen:
A far sea moves in my ear.

One cry, and I stumble from bed, cow-heavy and floral
In my Victorian nightgown.
15 Your mouth opens clean as a cat's. The window square

Whitens and swallows its dull stars. And now you try
Your handful of notes;
The clear vowels rise like balloons.

(*a*) Make a detailed analysis of Plath's poetic treatment of the relationship between mother and child in this poem.

(*b*) Go on to discuss distinctive aspects of her poetic treatment of the relationship between mother and child in **two** or **three** other poems.

24. The Scottish Ballads

Make a comparative study of some of the ways in which death is given significance in **three** or **four** Scottish ballads.

[Turn over

PROSE FICTION

25. Achebe

Discuss the significance within Achebe's fiction of his use of proverbs, popular adages, folktales and any other characteristics of Ibo language and culture that you think are important.

26. Austen

"***Emma*** *is a good-humoured, benevolent social comedy that never falters in its tone;* ***Persuasion*** *is an altogether darker novel, almost tragic in its implications and much more acerbic in its criticism of society.*"

How far do you agree?

27. Dickens

Examine Dickens's treatment of wealth and its effects upon the individual in *Great Expectations* **or** in *Bleak House* **or** in both novels.

28. Forster

Compare and contrast the role of Mrs Wilcox in *Howards End* with that of Mrs Moore in *A Passage to India*.

29. Galloway

Analyse and evaluate the means by which Galloway engages the reader with the inner lives of her main protagonists in *The Trick is to Keep Breathing* **and** in *Foreign Parts*.

30. Gray

Discuss the use of different narrative voices within *Lanark* **and** within *Poor Things*.

31. Gunn

The following extract is taken from ***Highland River.***

Read the extract carefully and then answer the questions that follow it.

An hour later, he left the white shore and encountered two or three tiny lochs, called dubh lochs. The inland moors were full of them. He had heard stories of their treacherous depths. The one in front of him was barely six feet across, its water hardly a foot deep. When his stick touched bottom in the middle it went sinking into the soft, 5 dark ooze under its own weight. With his finger tip and the slightest of pressures, he sank it its full five feet. He had only to take one step forward and not all his struggles or clawings at the bank would save him from being sucked to death.

He was aware of an irrational pleasure, arising out of an absolute absence of fear. He had once thought of Radzyn's mind as a remote place with chasms.

10 As he looked back at Loch Braighe na h'Aibhne, his lips moved in their characteristic humour, but in his eyes was a deep, secret tenderness.

The intimacy was very close now. In the last few moments before he had risen he had seen himself walking towards the mountain, much as, in the last year or two, he had seen the little figure of the boy Kenn adventuring into the strath. What older 15 mind, in this curious regress, was now the observer might be difficult to say, for its apprehension seemed profounder than individual thought. Pict, and Viking too, and Gael; the folk, through immense eras of time; sea and river, moor and loch; the abiding land: of which the departing figure was a silent emanation, more inevitable than any figure in any vision.

20 From the high summit, the solitary figure would watch the dawn come up behind the Orkneys; would see on the mountain ranges of Sutherland the grey planetary light that reveals the earth as a ball turning slowly in the immense chasm of space; would turn again to the plain of Caithness, that land of exquisite lights, and be held by a myriad lochs and dubh lochs glimmering blood-red. He could then bow his head and see what 25 lay in his heart and in his mind.

Kenn withdrew his eyes from the source of his river and, turning, saw about him here and there on the moor the golden spikes of the bog asphodel. He picked one and found it had a scent. He searched for the name of the scent and remembered the taste of a golden candy Sans used to sell out of a glass bottle. At that, little Kenn's face 30 vanished goblin-like across his mind. He could not all at once throw the flower from him nor could he put it in his buttonhole, so he forgot it in his hand as he went over the watershed and down into the valley that lay between him and the base of the mountain.

(*a*) Analyse in detail the means by which Gunn explores the relationship between Kenn and the natural world in this extract.

(*b*) Go on to discuss some of the ways in which Gunn gives significance to the natural world elsewhere in *Highland River* **or** in *The Silver Darlings*.

[Turn over

32. Hardy

"In Henchard and Tess Hardy presents us with characters who are responsible for their own suffering."

How far do you agree?

33. Hogg

Analyse the narrative structure of *The Private Memoirs and Confessions of a Justified Sinner* and comment on its effectiveness.

34. Joyce

Discuss the portrayal of young love in *A Portrait of the Artist as a Young Man* **and** in any **two** of the short stories from *Dubliners*.

35. Spark

The following extract is taken from the opening chapter of ***The Girls of Slender Means.***

Read the extract carefully and then answer the questions that follow it (Page twelve).

Long ago in 1945 all the nice people in England were poor, allowing for exceptions. The streets of the cities were lined with buildings in bad repair or in no repair at all, bomb-sites piled with stony rubble, houses like giant teeth in which decay had been drilled out, leaving only the cavity. Some bomb-ripped buildings looked like the ruins
5 of ancient castles until, at a closer view, the wallpapers of various quite normal rooms would be visible, room above room, exposed, as on a stage, with one wall missing; sometimes a lavatory chain would dangle over nothing from a fourth- or fifth-floor ceiling; most of all the staircases survived, like a new art-form, leading up and up to an unspecified destination that made unusual demands on the mind's eye. All the nice
10 people were poor; at least, that was a general axiom, the best of the rich being poor in spirit.

There was absolutely no point in feeling depressed about the scene, it would have been like feeling depressed about the Grand Canyon or some event of the earth outside everybody's scope. People continued to exchange assurances of depressed feelings
15 about the weather or the news, or the Albert Memorial which had not been hit, not even shaken, by any bomb from first to last.

The May of Teck Club stood obliquely opposite the site of the Memorial, in one of a row of tall houses which had endured, but barely; some bombs had dropped nearby, and in a few back gardens, leaving the buildings cracked on the outside and shakily
20 hinged within, but habitable for the time being. The shattered windows had been replaced with new glass rattling in loose frames. More recently, the bituminous black-out paint had been removed from landing and bathroom windows. Windows were important in that year of final reckoning; they told at a glance whether a house was inhabited or not; and in the course of the past years they had accumulated much
25 meaning, having been the main danger-zone between domestic life and the war going on outside: everyone had said, when the sirens sounded, "Mind the windows. Keep away from the windows. Watch out for the glass."

The May of Teck Club had been three times window-shattered since 1940, but never directly hit. There the windows of the upper bedrooms overlooked the dip and
30 rise of treetops in Kensington Gardens across the street, with the Albert Memorial to

be seen by means of a slight craning and twist of the neck. These upper bedrooms looked down on the opposite pavement on the park side of the street, and on the tiny people who moved along in neat-looking singles and couples, pushing little prams loaded with pin-head babies and provisions, or carrying little dots of shopping bags.
35 Everyone carried a shopping bag in case they should be lucky enough to pass a shop that had a sudden stock of something off the rations.

From the lower-floor dormitories the people in the street looked larger, and the paths of the park were visible. All the nice people were poor, and few were nicer, as nice people come, than these girls at Kensington who glanced out of the windows in the
40 early mornings to see what the day looked like, or gazed out on the green summer evenings, as if reflecting on the months ahead, on love and the relations of love. Their eyes gave out an eager-spirited light that resembled near-genius, but was youth merely. The first of the Rules of Constitution, drawn up at some remote and innocent Edwardian date, still applied more or less to them:

45 The May of Teck Club exists for the Pecuniary Convenience and Social Protection of Ladies of Slender Means below the age of Thirty Years, who are obliged to reside apart from their Families in order to follow an Occupation in London.

As they realized themselves in varying degrees, few people alive at the time were more delightful, more ingenious, more movingly lovely, and, as it might happen, more
50 savage, than the girls of slender means.

*

"I've got something to tell you," said Jane Wright, the woman columnist.

At the other end of the telephone, the voice of Dorothy Markham, owner of the flourishing model agency, said, "Darling, where have you been?" She spoke, by habit since her débutante days, with the utmost enthusiasm of tone.

55 "I've got something to tell you. Do you remember Nicholas Farringdon? Remember he used to come to the old May of Teck just after the war, he was an anarchist and poet sort of thing. A tall man with—"

"The one that got on to the roof to sleep out with Selina?"

"Yes, Nicholas Farringdon."

60 "Oh rather. Has he turned up?"

"No, he's been martyred."

"What-ed?"

"Martyred in Haiti. Killed. Remember he became a Brother—"

"But I've just been to Tahiti, it's marvellous, everyone's marvellous. Where did you
65 hear it?"

"Haiti. There's a news paragraph just come over Reuters. I'm sure it's the same Nicholas Farringdon because it says a missionary, former poet. I nearly died. I knew him well, you know, in those days. I expect they'll hush it all up, about those days, if they want to make a martyr story."

70 "How did it happen, is it gruesome?"

"Oh, I don't know, there's only a paragraph."

"You'll have to find out more through your grapevine. I'm shattered. I've got heaps to tell you."

*

The Committee of Management wishes to express surprise at the Members' protest
75 regarding the wallpaper chosen for the drawing room. The Committee wishes to point out that Members' residential fees do not meet the running expenses of the Club. The Committee regrets that the spirit of the May of Teck foundation has apparently so far deteriorated that such a protest has been made. The Committee refers Members to the terms of the Club's Foundation.

80 Joanna Childe was a daughter of a country rector. She had a good intelligence and strong obscure emotions. She was training to be a teacher of elocution and, while attending a school of drama, already had pupils of her own. Joanna Childe had been drawn to this profession by her good voice and love of poetry which she loved rather as it might be assumed a cat loves birds; poetry, especially the declamatory sort, excited
85 and possessed her; she would pounce on the stuff, play with it quivering in her mind, and when she had got it by heart, she spoke it forth with devouring relish. Mostly, she indulged the habit while giving elocution lessons at the club where she was highly thought of for it. The vibrations of Joanna's elocution voice from her room or from the recreation room where she frequently rehearsed, were felt to add tone and style to
90 the establishment when boy-friends called. Her taste in poetry became the accepted taste of the club. She had a deep feeling for certain passages in the authorized version of the Bible, besides the Book of Common Prayer, Shakespeare and Gerard Manley Hopkins, and had newly discovered Dylan Thomas. She was not moved by the poetry of Eliot and Auden, except for the latter's lyric:

95 Lay your sleeping head, my love,
Human on my faithless arm;

Joanna Childe was large, with light shiny hair, blue eyes and deep-pink cheeks. When she read the notice signed by Lady Julia Markham, chairwoman of the committee, she stood with the other young women round the green baize board and
100 was given to murmur:

"He rageth, and again he rageth, because he knows his time is short."

It was not known to many that this was a reference to the Devil, but it caused amusement. She had not intended it so. It was not usual for Joanna to quote anything for its aptitude, and at conversational pitch.

(*a*) Identify the distinctive aspects of Spark's narrative method evident in this extract.

(*b*) How far are such aspects as you have identified characteristic of her narrative method elsewhere in this novel **and** in *The Prime of Miss Jean Brodie*?

36. Stevenson

How important is Stevenson's evocation of mood and atmosphere to the success of *The Strange Case of Dr Jekyll and Mr Hyde* **and** of *Weir of Hermiston*?

PROSE NON-FICTION

37. Autobiography

In what ways have any **two** of the specified autobiographies contributed to your interest in and understanding of the times in which the writers lived?

38. Autobiography

How effectively does the writer reveal or create or explore his or her identity in any **one** of the specified autobiographies?

39. Travel Writing

"*Representations of place often tell us more about the culture of the writer than about the culture of the place or places visited.*"

Discuss with reference to **one** or **more than one** of the specified texts.

40. Travel Writing

"*In many ways, the best travel writers work like novelists: they select; they cast light on this object or shadow on that; they shape character; they imagine.*"

Discuss the work of **one** or **more than one** of the travel writers you have studied in the light of this assertion.

41. Writing about Scotland

"*Writing about Scotland from the last hundred years is marked by a bleakness of vision, by anger and dismay at what the writer observes.*"

Discuss with detailed reference to any **two** of the specified texts.

42. Writing about Scotland

"*There is no such thing as a Scottish national identity; what there is is a multiplicity of small local identities.*"

To what extent is this view reflected in **one** or **more than one** of the specified texts?

[Turn over

Section 2—Language Study

You must answer **one question only** in this section.

Topic A—The use of English in a particular geographical area

1. Describe the distinctive linguistic features of a particular regional variety of English and go on to discuss **one** or **more than one** of the following: who speaks it, its history, its relationship to other regional varieties, its relationship to Standard English, the contexts in which it is used.

2. Describe in detail the vocabulary, grammar and pronunciation of a particular overseas variety of English.

Topic B—Variations in the use of English related to social class

3. "*People's perception of linguistic differences across social classes has more to do with their prejudices than with any substantial variations in language use.*"

How far do you agree?

You should support your answer with detailed reference to vocabulary, grammar and pronunciation.

4. If you were to investigate the relationship between language and social class, how would you collect your data and how would you analyse it?

Topic C—Variations in the use of English related to gender

5. Some researchers have claimed that in male-female conversations men's talk is more competitive and less co-operative than that of women.

What evidence can be drawn upon to support or challenge such a claim?

6. From your own experience and from your reading and research, compare and contrast the typical features of conversation in male-only groups with the typical features of conversation in female-only groups.

Topic D—The linguistic characteristics of informal conversation

For both questions on this topic (see *Page sixteen*), you are provided with a transcript of a conversational exchange between Addie and Brianne, two young American women.

NB The examples used to illustrate the transcription key that precedes the transcript are **not** taken from the transcript itself.

Each line of the transcript contains a single intonation unit, and the conventions of transcription are as follows:

Transcription Key

She's out. — *A full stop shows falling tone in the preceding element.*
Oh yeah? — *A question mark shows rising tone in the preceding element.*
Well, okay — *A comma indicates a continuing intonation, drawing out the preceding element.*
Damn — *Italics show heavy stress.*
bu–but? — *A single dash indicates a cut-off with a glottal stop.*
says "Oh" — *Double quotes mark speech that is set off by a shift in the speaker's voice.*
[and so-] — *Square brackets on successive lines mark the beginning and end of*
[Why] her? *overlapping talk.*
{sigh} — *Curly brackets enclose editorial comments.*

Transcript

1	Addie:	you know my mom and I went to Monroe today.
2	Brianne:	uh-huh
3	Addie:	and anyway, so –
4		Keith swore that it was Sheila in the car.
5		now Sheila heard all this through Alison.
6		because Alison, I guess, worked today.
7		and, um, sh–
8		he swore that it was her riding in the car. {laughs}
9	Brianne:	{laughing} no way.
10	Addie:	and I guess he said to Alison,
11		cause Alison, um,
12		he asked her, Alison,
13		if she could stay a little later
14		and she said "No,
15		because I have to go to Monroe to get some things,
16		y'know I have to run some errands."
17		and he thought that it was a scam
18		that Sheila was going with them.
19	Brianne:	oh, no.
20	Addie:	and that's why Sheila didn't come in to work.
21	Brianne:	oh, no.

22	Addie:	and so he said, y'know,
23		"I–If I find out that–
24		that you and Sheila were in Monroe
25		you *both* are going to be fired" {laughs}
26	Brianne:	"yeah, sure,
27		go ahead and fire them, y'know,
28		then you could just work that much more, Keith,
29		y'know, you want to work forty hours a day,
30		don't you?"
31	Addie:	{laughing} and so I guess, Sheila,
32		[Sheila was so mad]
33	Brianne:	[oh, man.]
34		not to trust your employees at all.
35	Addie:	yeah.

[Source: Neal R. Norrick (2000) *Conversational Narrative: Storytelling in Everyday Talk* Amsterdam/Philadelphia: John Benjamins, pp 210–11 ISBN 90–272–3710–7]

7. How typical do you find this extract as an example of storytelling in informal conversation?

In answering this question, you should discuss matters such as narrative structures, interactions between speakers and the purposes of storytelling in informal conversations.

8. What choices are involved in transcribing speech? Base your answer on the transcript given above and on your study of other transcripts of informal conversation.

Topic E—The linguistic characteristics of political communication

9. Describe and give examples of the kinds of linguistic strategies used by politicians to:

- present their own party's image
- comment on rival parties' statements and actions
- represent particular events.

10. In this question you are provided with an excerpt from the *Official Report* of the Scottish Parliament (8th September 2004). This excerpt is an edited transcript (in which for ease of reference each paragraph is numbered) of a debate following the First Minister's Question Time of the previous day. On that day, the First Minister, Jack McConnell, had outlined his government's economic strategy.

How effective do you find this excerpt as an example of political communication?

In answering this question, you should examine as many of the following as you consider appropriate:

- the conventions of debates such as this
- the degree of formality
- the choice of vocabulary
- the degree of grammatical complexity
- the description of rival parties
- the use of humour.

[1] **Mr Ted Brocklebank (Mid Scotland and Fife) (Con)**: I want to explore in further detail some of the things that the First Minister said yesterday and, perhaps more important, some of the things that he did not say.

[2] A couple of years ago, Jack McConnell said that his Executive was going to "do less, better". If that were an alternative to doing a lot of things badly, few could question the logic. However, it turned out that, while the coalition was, indeed, doing fewer things, it was not necessarily doing them better. So, as we discovered in yesterday's statement, it is time to raise the goalposts again. The softly-softly approach has been abandoned, and no fewer than 12 major pieces of legislation will be introduced this year. However, as we say in my part of Fife, it is a poor cadger that shouts "stinking fish".

[3] I had to pinch myself to realise that the litany of supposed achievements and aspirations that the First Minister was talking up yesterday had happened in the same small country that I live in. Like Jack McConnell, I believe that Scotland is one of the best small countries in the world. However, I believe that despite, rather than because of, the efforts of the coalition. The coalition had nothing to do with the creation of our wonderful scenery—although its policies, in particular those on wind farms, might go a long way towards destroying it. The coalition has done nothing to improve the quality of Scottish education, which was once recognised as of international class but which is now too often regarded as second rate. The coalition has turned the thrifty, entrepreneurial country that Scotland once was into a land in which one in every four employees works in a public sector that accounts for an extraordinary 52 per cent of the country's gross domestic product.

[4] However, this week, Jack McConnell seems to have seen the light. His latest big media message is that the balance between the public and private sectors has swung too far in favour of the state and must be redressed, but—wait for it—that will be done not by reducing the public sector in places such as Fife, where council employment has increased by another 5 per cent, or 600 employees, this year, but by increasing the private sector. Apparently, we can do one but we cannot do the other. Does the First Minister intend to follow Gordon Brown's example and make public service job cuts? If he does not, was his latest soundbite an example of how he intends to raise the game in Parliamentary debates?

[5] **Christine May (Central Fife) (Lab)**: Will the member give way?

[6] **Mr Brocklebank**: A little later, perhaps.

[7] I am reminded of my days in the Salvation Army and the old hymn:
"Tell me the old, old story, for I forget so soon . . .
Tell me the story simply, as to a little child
For I am weak and weary and helpless and defiled."
I expect that that strikes a chord with many Scots as we enter this Executive's sixth year.

[8] **Christine May**: Mr Brocklebank talked about the increases in public sector employment. Given that most of those employees are teachers, social workers and workers in the health service, will he tell us how many doctors, nurses and social workers the Tories would get rid of?

[9] **Mr Brocklebank**: In Christine May's part of Fife—the part that we both come from—by far the largest employer is the public sector. Indeed, that is true for the whole of Fife. I will not guess at how many teachers, doctors and others there are, but is Christine May happy with that statistic? I do not believe so.

[10] Jack McConnell told members that his job is not to create jobs, but to create the climate in which enterprise, innovation and risk taking can grow. That sounded great until he sat down after more than an hour without having once mentioned the Scottish industry that led the world in risk taking, innovation and sheer hard work. Of course, I am talking about the Scottish fishing industry.

[11] **Jeremy Purvis (Tweeddale, Ettrick and Lauderdale) (LD)**: Will the member give way?

[12] **Mr Brocklebank**: A little later, perhaps.

[End]

[Source:http://www.scottish.parliament.uk/business/officialReports/meetingsParliament/archive/or-04/sor0908-02.htm#Col10024]

Topic F—The linguistic characteristics of tabloid journalism

11. For this question, you are provided with an extract from *The Sun* newspaper of Friday, September 3, 2004.

Make a detailed analysis of the page provided in which you identify and discuss those aspects of style and language which a reader would expect of tabloid journalism.

WE BEAT BARMY PARLY BAN

Crunch talks . . . Tory MSP Bill Aitken enjoys our toast outside the parliament yesterday and thanks Sun man Kenny for bringing him breakfast

THE SCOTTISH Sun IS THE TOAST OF HOLYROOD

MSPs line up for our breakfast

By KENNY MCALPINE

HUNGRY Holyrood MSPs found out which side their bread is buttered on—after we served them up some tasty TOAST.

We revealed yesterday how crusty parly bosses banned the breakfast dish in case it sets off smoke alarms.

Hot topic . . . our story

But we were the toast of Holyrood when we set up our own brekkie stall outside their offices.

Equipped with dozens of loaves and a toaster, we gave away free buttered toast to hundreds of MSPs and parly workers. Tory MSP Bill Aitken said: "Had it not been for the Scottish Sun we would not have been able to get our toast today.

"It is ridiculous that we can spend £430 million on a parliament building but we cannot make or eat toast in it."

The Executive banned the making of toast after smoke from the kitchens' toasters caused a spate of false fire alerts.

Burnt offering . . . toaster pops up

Buttering 'em up . . . Kenny feeds grateful workers

12. With reference to content and style, mode of address and typical stance, discuss how any **one** tabloid newspaper presents its view of the world.

If you choose to discuss *The Sun* newspaper in your answer to this question, you may include reference to the text provided for question 11.

Topic G—The use of Scots in a particular geographical area

13. What have you observed about the use of the Scots language in the 21st century?

In your answer you must refer in detail to your own research and you may refer to **one** or **more than one** geographical area.

14. What are the main influences that have shaped Scots vocabulary in **one** or **more than one** geographical area?

Topic H—The linguistic characteristics of Scots as used in informal conversation

15. From your own systematic study, identify and describe some of the ways you or other people you know or have observed use Scots in informal conversation.

16. Discuss the ways in which Scots is used in the following transcript.

The transcript is part of a conversation involving Annie and Joe, who live beside a railway, and Neil, their neighbour. Annie tells the story of her daughter Jean's poodle, Cherie. The text is lightly transcribed as follows.

<NA>XXXX<NA>	signifies inaudible speech
<NA>laughs</NV>	signifies non-verbal behaviour
<-->	signifies pause

	Annie:	Many a cat we lost on that railway.
	Joe:	Ken what we used tae like on the railway? See when they –
5	**Annie**:	They used tae go past. The puffies, the puffies used tae go past and they flung aw the coal off in the garden, Neil, and ye went oot and there was huge coal . . . Oh!
	Joe:	Aye, the old steam-tails went past, Neil. And they cairted the coal. And they <NA>XXXX<NA> there <NA>XXXX<NA> there the boy that <NA>XXXX<NA> the coal. Big lumps is rollin oot the door, rollin oot the door, rolling oot the door.
10	**Neil**:	<NV>laughs</NV>
	Joe:	. . . an eh we'd tae get along wae the barrie, Neil eh? . . . And we used tae go through wi' the barrie and get the coal and all them . . . Aye, we used tae walk that line and that.
15	**Annie:**	And then they used tae throw it in the garden. As <--> Ken the bit at the back? They used tae full it fu' for us and hoot their horn . . . And then, on a Sunday we'd to hurry and get the coal, and then, on a Sunday there was nae trains, ye see, so ye could walk the line on a Sunday and pick up aw the coal up ye wanted.

Neil: Good god.

20 **Joe**: Aye a whole lot o coal and that.

Annie: It was great in they days! And then the puffies came along and all the bankins used tae go on fire . . . ye see?

Neil: Aye.

Annie: So they had tae beat the fire oot, and the fire-engines used tae hae tae come
25 and put aw the fires oot. There was nae g- overgrown bankings then. It was bare.

Joe: Tell Neil aboot yer wee dug eh? 'Cross the railway.

Annie: Oh aye the poodle.

Joe: Aye.

30 **Annie:** We'd a wee poodle, and Jean's <--> Jean's poodle, but she went away up the wood on her bike round the road.

Joe: 'Cross the railway. Ken there was a walkway cross the railway. Ken sleepers how ye walked on them to the signal-box.

Neil: Uhuh.

35 **Annie:** And Cherie was in, and I says, "Don't let Cherie see where ye're goin." Well, Cherie sh- f- <--> got oot and smelt Jean and she crossed the train, and the train was comin and the driver couldnae stop. So, of course, she fell, and she fell in the middle of the track.

Joe: It was lucky, aye.

40 **Annie:** And she was alive. And I rushed her to the vet, but she had holes in her back wae the big stones, and the buffer hit her.

Joe: So we rushed her to the vet . . . It was the big chains. No, it was the big chains that hung doun. And the vet s- <--> hit her <--> And the vet said tae me, "If she lives the night, she'll live."

45 **Annie:** It wasnae the buffer, Neil, it was the snow-plough on the front . . . Oh that hit the wag- <--> that hit the wag- <--> oh aye hit her. Lucky it never killed her!

Neil: Mhm.

Annie: So she lived, but she was very badly hurt. Well, no many months ago,
50 there was a man came intae the mill and he says tae me, "I often wonder about yer wee poodle."

Neil: Aye?

Annie: "For," he says, "I noticed that she ran on the railway and you were gonna run efter her and I'm sayin tae mysel, 'Dinnae run on that railway' for I
55 was drivin the train." And he says, "Ye were a young lassie then, and I'm sayin, 'Oh dinnae run on the railway, dinnae run on the railway.'"

Neil: Oh he was the driver!

Annie: He was the driver!

[Turn over

	Joe:	He was the driver.
60	**Annie**:	And he says, "What happened tae the poodle?" and I says, "The poodle lived, she lived." And I says, "She was badly hurt, but she lived."
	Neil:	Mm.
	Annie:	And he says, "Oh my god, I've often thocht aboot that." And he says, "I was just wonderin if you were gonna move or no tae grab her, because I
65		could never stoapped."
	Neil:	Aye.

Topic I—Variations in the use of Scots among older and younger people

17. "*From at least the first half of the eighteenth century, Scots has always been thought to be 'dying out' as a spoken language.*"

Introduction to the Concise Scots Dictionary

Based upon your research into variations in the use of Scots among older and younger people in the 21st century, do **you** think that Scots is "*dying out*" as a spoken language?

18. To what extent has Scots been maintained and adapted for contemporary use (for example, in the home, in the workplace, in the community)?

In answering this question, you should make detailed reference to your own study of the use of Scots among older and younger people.

Topic J—Uses of Scots in the media

19. Choose a television or radio programme or series of programmes which has made significant use of Scots. Describe in detail how Scots is used in the programme or series of programmes you have chosen.

20. "*There's no longer such a thing as BBC English. Voices of all varieties are mainstreamed into broadcast media.*"

In the light of this statement, discuss the range of Scots voices heard in broadcast media.

Topic K—Uses of Scots in contemporary literature

21. Analyse and evaluate the use of Scots in the work of **one** or **more than one** novelist or short story writer you have studied.

22. Compare and contrast the use of Scots in the following poem, *Sharleen: Ah'm Shy*, by Janet Paisley, with the use of Scots in the extract from the poem, *Almost Miss Scotland*, by Liz Lochhead.

You should examine vocabulary, grammar, pronunciation, orthography or any other features you think significant.

SHARLEEN: AH'M SHY

Ah'm shy. Aye, ah am. Canny look naebody in the eye.
Ah've seen me go in a shoap an jist hoap naebody wid talk tae me.
Things that happen, likesae—yer oot fur a walk
and some bloke whits never even spoke afore goes by
an he's given ye the eye. See me, ah jist want tae die.
Ah go rid tae the roots o ma hair. Weel it's no fair, is it?
Feel a right twit. See ma Ma. She says it'll pass.
'Ye'll grow oot o it hen.' Aye, aw right. But when?
Ye kin get awfy fed up bein the local beetroot.
So last time I went oot—tae the disco—
ah bought this white make-up. White lightening it said.
Ah thought, nae beamers the night, this stuff'll see me aw right.
Onywey, there ah wis, actin it. Daen ma pale an intrestin bit.
White lightening. See unner them flashin lights
it was quite frightnin. Cause ma face looked aw blue.
See, when a think o it noo, it was mortifyin.
Cause they aw thought ah wis dyin, an they dialled 999.
Fine thing tae be, centre o awbody's attention, me.
They hud me sat oan this chair, bit when they brought stretchers in,
ah slid oantae the flair—an jist lay there.
Ah thought, rule number one, when ye've made a fool o yersell
dinnae let oan, play the game. So ah let oot a groan an lay still.
Until this ambulance fella feels ma wrist,
an then he gies ma neck a twist—an ye'll no believe this.
Bit right there and then—he gies me a kiss.
Blew intae ma mooth, honest. God'strewth ah wis gasping fur breath.
Jist goes tae show yer no safe, naeplace these days.
Onywey ah blew right back, that made him move quick.
Fur he says are you aw right, are ye gaun tae be sick.
That's when ah noticed his eyes—they were daurk broon.
An staring right intae them made ma stomach go roon.
Ah felt kinda queer, an he says, c'mon we'll get ye oot o here.
Bit ah made him take me right hame—though ah'm seein him again,
the morra. Aw the same, how kin ah tell him dae ye suppose,
that when ye kiss a lassie, ye dinnae haud her nose?

Janet Paisley

[Turn over

ALMOST MISS SCOTLAND

The night I
Almost became Miss Scotland,
I caused a big stramash
When I sashayed on in my harristweed heathermix onepiece
And my "Miss Garthamlock" sash.

I wis six-fit-six, I wis slinky
(Yet nae skinnymalinky) —
My waist was nipped in wi elastic,
My powder and panstick were three inches thick,
Nails? Long, blood-rid and plastic.
So my big smile'd come across, I'd larded oan lipgloss
And my false eyelashes were mink
With a sky blue crescent that was pure iridescent
When I lowered my eyelids to blink.

Well, I wiggled tapselteerie, my heels were that peerie
While a kinna Jimmy Shandish band
Played "Flower of Scotland"—
But it aw got droont oot wi wolf whistles —
And that's no countin "For These Are My Mountains"
— See I'd tits like nuclear missiles.

Then this familiar-lukkin felly
I'd seen a loat oan the telly
Interviewed me aboot my hobbies —
I says: Macrame, origami,
Being nice tae my mammy —
(Basically I tellt him a loat o jobbies).
I was givin it that
Aboot my ambition to chat
To handicapped and starvin children from other nations
— How I was certain I'd find
Travel wid broaden my mind
As I fulfilled my Miss Scotland obligations.

Liz Lochhead

Topic L—Uses of Scots in specialised fields

23. According to the Scottish Parliament's website, the Cross Party Group on the Scots Language exists to "*promote the cause of Scots, inform members of the culture and heritage of the language and highlight the need for action to support Scots*".

Discuss how "the culture and heritage" of the Scots language might be promoted in **one** or **more than one** specialised field you have studied.

24. Describe and account for the Scots used in **one** or **more than one** specialised field. You might consider examples from Agriculture, Fishing, the Church, the Law, the Building Trade, Place Names, Street Names or any other specialised field about which you have knowledge.

Section 3—Textual Analysis

You must answer **one question only** in this section.

1. Prose fiction [*Pages twenty-five to twenty-nine*]

The following extract is taken from Chapter Two of the novel ***Brick Lane (2003)*** *by Monica Ali.*

Read the extract carefully and then answer the following question.

Analyse Monica Ali's presentation of Chanu and of Nazneen and of their relationship:

- in the course of the dinner party (lines 1–130)
- in the remainder of the extract (lines 131–200).

Dr Azad was a small, precise man who, contrary to the Bengali custom, spoke at a level only one quarter of a decibel above a whisper. Anyone who wished to hear what he was saying was obliged to lean in towards him, so that all evening Chanu gave the appearance of hanging on his every word.

5 "Come," said Dr Azad, when Nazneen was hovering behind the table ready to serve. "Come and sit down with us."

"My wife is very shy." Chanu smiled and motioned with his head for her to be seated.

"This week I saw two of our young men in a very sorry state," said the doctor. "I 10 told them straight, this is your choice: stop drinking alcohol now, or by Eid your liver will be finished. Ten years ago this would be unthinkable. Two in one week! But now our children are copying what they see here, going to the pub, to nightclubs. Or drinking at home in their bedrooms where their parents think they are perfectly safe. The problem is our community is not properly educated about these things." Dr Azad 15 drank a glass of water down in one long draught and poured himself another. "I always drink two glasses before starting the meal." He drank the second glass. "Good. Now I will not overeat."

"Eat! Eat!" said Chanu. "Water is good for cleansing the system, but food is also essential." He scooped up lamb and rice with his fingers and chewed. He put too 20 much in his mouth at once, and he made sloppy noises as he ate. When he could speak again, he said, "I agree with you. Our community is not educated about this, and much else besides. But for my part, I don't plan to risk these things happening to my children. We will go back before they get spoiled."

"This is another disease that afflicts us," said the doctor. "I call it Going Home 25 Syndrome. Do you know what that means?" He addressed himself to Nazneen.

She felt a heat on the back of her neck and formed words that did not leave her mouth.

"It is natural," said Chanu. "These people are basically peasants and they miss the land. The pull of the land is stronger even than the pull of blood."

30 "And when they have saved enough they will get on an aeroplane and go?"

"They don't ever really leave home. Their bodies are here but their hearts are back there. And anyway, look how they live: just recreating the villages here."

"But they will never save enough to go back." Dr Azad helped himself to vegetables. His shirt was spotless white, and his collar and tie so high under his chin
35 that he seemed to be missing a neck. Nazneen saw an oily yellow stain on her husband's shirt where he had dripped food.

Dr Azad continued, "Every year they think, just one more year. But whatever they save, it's never enough."

"We would not need very much," said Nazneen. Both men looked at her. She
40 spoke to her plate. "I mean, we could live very cheaply." The back of her neck burned.

Chanu filled the silence with his laugh. "My wife is just settling in here." He coughed and shuffled in his chair. "The thing is, with the promotion coming up, things are beginning to go well for me now. If I just get the promotion confirmed then
45 many things are possible."

"I used to think all the time of going back," said Dr Azad. He spoke so quietly that Nazneen was forced to look directly at him, because to catch all the words she had to follow his lips. "Every year I thought, 'Maybe this year.' And I'd go for a visit, buy some more land, see relatives and friends and make up my mind to return for good.
50 But something would always happen. A flood, a tornado that just missed the building, a power cut, some mind-numbing piece of petty bureaucracy, bribes to be paid out to get anything done. And I'd think, 'Well, maybe not this year.' And now, I don't know. I just don't know."

Chanu cleared his throat. "Of course, it's not been announced yet. Other people
55 have applied. But after my years of service . . . Do you know, in six years I have not been late on one single day! And only three sick days, even with the ulcer. Some of my colleagues are very unhealthy, always going off sick with this or that. It's not something I could bring to Mr Dalloway's attention. Even so, I feel he ought to be aware of it."

60 "I wish you luck," said Dr Azad.

"Then there's the academic perspective. Within months I will be a fully fledged academic with two degrees. One from a British university. Bachelor of Arts degree. With honours."

"I'm sure you have a good chance."

65 "Did Mr Dalloway tell you that?"

"Who's that?"

"Mr Dalloway."

The doctor shrugged his neat shoulders.

"My superior. Mr Dalloway. He told you I have a good chance?"

70 "No."

"He said I didn't have a good chance?"

"He didn't say anything at all. I don't know the gentleman in question."

"He's one of your patients. His secretary made an appointment for him to see you about his shoulder sprain. He's a squash player. Very active man. Average build, I'd
75 say. Red hair. Wears contact lenses—perhaps you test his eyes as well."

"It's possible he's a patient. There are several thousand on the list for my practice."

"What I should have told you straight away—he has a harelip. Well, it's been put right, reconstructive surgery and all that, but you can always tell. That should put you on to him."

80 The guest remained quiet. Nazneen heard Chanu suppress a belch. She wanted to go to him and stroke his forehead. She wanted to get up from the table and walk out of the door and never see him again.

"He might be a patient. I do not know him." It was nearly a whisper.

"No," said Chanu. "I see."

85 "But I wish you luck."

"I am forty years old," said Chanu. He spoke quietly like the doctor, with none of his assurance. "I have been in this country for sixteen years. Nearly half my life." He gave a dry-throated gargle. "When I came I was a young man. I had ambitions. Big dreams. When I got off the aeroplane I had my degree certificate in my suitcase and a 90 few pounds in my pocket. I thought there would be a red carpet laid out for me. I was going to join the Civil Service and become Private Secretary to the Prime Minister." As he told his story, his voice grew. It filled the room. "That was my plan. And then I found things were a bit different. These people here didn't know the difference between me, who stepped off an aeroplane with a degree certificate, and the peasants 95 who jumped off the boat possessing only the lice on their heads. What can you do?" He rolled a ball of rice and meat in his fingers and teased it around his plate.

"I did this and that. Whatever I could. So much hard work, so little reward. More or less it is true to say I have been chasing wild buffaloes and eating my own rice. You know that saying? All the begging letters from home I burned. And I made two 100 promises to myself. I will be a success, come what may. That's promise number one. Number two, I will go back home. When I am a success. And I will honour these promises." Chanu, who had grown taller and taller in his chair, sank back down.

"Very good, very good," said Dr Azad. He checked his watch.

"The begging letters still come," said Chanu. "From old servants, from the 105 children of servants. Even from my own family, although they are not in need. All they can think of is money. They think there is gold lying about in the streets here and I am just hoarding it all in my palace. But I did not come here for money. Was I starving in Dhaka? I was not. Do they enquire about my diplomas?" He gestured to the wall, where various framed certificates were displayed. "They do not. What is 110 more . . ." He cleared his throat, although it was already clear. Dr Azad looked at Nazneen and, without meaning to, she returned his gaze so that she was caught in a complicity of looks, given and returned, which said something about her husband that she ought not to be saying.

Chanu talked on. Dr Azad finished the food on his plate while Chanu's food grew 115 cold. Nazneen picked at the cauliflower curry. The doctor declined with a waggle of the head either a further helping or any dessert. He sat with his hands folded on the table while Chanu, his oration at an end, ate noisily and quickly. Twice more he checked his watch.

[Turn over

At half past nine Dr Azad said, "Well, Chanu. I thank you and your wife for a most
120 pleasant evening and a delicious meal."

Chanu protested that it was still early. The doctor was adamant. "I always retire at ten thirty and I always read for half an hour in bed before that."

"We intellectuals must stick together," said Chanu, and he walked with his guest to the door.

125 "If you take my advice, one intellectual to another, you will eat more slowly, chew more thoroughly and take only a small portion of meat. Otherwise I'll see you back at the clinic again with another ulcer."

"Just think," said Chanu, "if I did not have the ulcer in the first place, then we would not have met and we would not have had this dinner together."

130 "Just think," said the doctor. He waved stiffly and disappeared behind the door.

The television was on. Chanu liked to keep it glowing in the evenings, like a fire in the corner of the room. Sometimes he went over and stirred it by pressing the buttons so that the light flared and changed colours. Mostly he ignored it. Nazneen held a pile of the last dirty dishes to take to the kitchen, but the screen held her. A man in a very
135 tight suit (so tight that it made his private parts stand out on display) and a woman in a skirt that did not even cover her bottom gripped each other as an invisible force hurtled them across an oval arena. The people in the audience clapped their hands together and then stopped. By some magic they all stopped at exactly the same time. The couple broke apart. They fled from each other and no sooner had they fled than they
140 sought each other out. Every move they made was urgent, intense, a declaration. The woman raised one leg and rested her boot (Nazneen saw the thin blade for the first time) on the other thigh, making a triangular flag of her legs, and spun around until she would surely fall but didn't. She did not slow down. She stopped dead and flung her arms above her head with a look so triumphant that you knew she had conquered
145 everything: her body, the laws of nature, and the heart of the tight-suited man who slid over on his knees, vowing to lay down his life for her.

"What is this called?" said Nazneen.

Chanu glanced at the screen. "Ice skating," he said, in English.

"Ice e-skating," said Nazneen.

150 "Ice skating," said Chanu.

"Ice e-skating."

"No, no. No *e*. Ice skating. Try it again."

Nazneen hesitated.

"Go on!"

155 "Ice es-kating," she said, with deliberation.

Chanu smiled. "Don't worry about it. It's a common problem for Bengalis. Two consonants together causes a difficulty. I have conquered this issue after a long time. But you are unlikely to need these words in any case."

"I would like to learn some English," said Nazneen.

160 Chanu puffed his cheeks and spat the air out in a *fuff*. "It will come. Don't worry about it. Where's the need anyway?" He looked at his book and Nazneen watched the screen.

"He thinks he will get the promotion because he goes to the *pub* with the boss. He is so stupid he doesn't even realize there is any other way of getting promotion."
165 Chanu was supposed to be studying. His books were open at the table. Every so often he looked in one, or turned a page. Mostly, he talked. *Pub, pub, pub*. Nazneen turned the word over in her mind. Another drop of English that she knew. There were other English words that Chanu sprinkled into his conversation, other things she could say to the tattoo lady. At this moment she could not think of any.

170 "This Wilkie—I told you about him—he has one or maybe two O levels. Every lunchtime he goes to the pub and he comes back half an hour late. Today I saw him sitting in Mr Dalloway's office using the phone with his feet up on the desk. The jackfruit is still on the tree but already he is oiling his moustache. No way is he going to get promoted."

175 Nazneen stared at the television. There was a close-up of the woman. She had sparkly bits around her eyes like tiny sequins glued to her face. Her hair was scraped back and tied on top of her head with plastic flowers. Her chest pumped up and down as if her heart would shoot out and she smiled pure, gold joy. She must be terrified, thought Nazneen, because such things cannot be held, and must be lost.

180 "No," said Chanu. "I don't have anything to fear from Wilkie. I have a degree from Dhaka University in English Literature. Can Wilkie quote from Chaucer or Dickens or Hardy?"

Nazneen, who feared her husband would begin one of his long quotations, stacked a final plate and went to the kitchen. He liked to quote in English and then give her a
185 translation, phrase by phrase. And when it was translated it usually meant no more to her than it did in English, so that she did not know what to reply or even if a reply was required.

She washed the dishes and rinsed them and Chanu came and leaned against the ill-fitting cupboards and talked some more. "You see," he said, a frequent opener
190 although often she did not see, "it is the white underclass, like Wilkie, who are most afraid of people like me. To him, and people like him, we are the only thing standing in the way of them sliding totally to the bottom of the pile. As long as we are below them, then they are above something. If they see us rise then they are resentful because we have left our proper place. That is why you get the phenomenon of the
195 *National Front*. They can play on those fears to create racial tensions, and give these people a superiority complex. The middle classes are more secure, and therefore more relaxed." He drummed his fingers against the Formica.

Nazneen took a tea towel and dried the plates. She wondered if the ice e-skating woman went home and washed and wiped. It was difficult to imagine. But there were
200 no servants here. She would have to manage by herself.

[Turn over

2. Prose non-fiction [*Pages thirty to thirty-one*]

The following extract is taken from ***Sea Burial*** *(1998) by James Hamilton-Paterson. This reflective section comes after the discovery at sea of a dead fisherman in his boat.*

Read the extract carefully and then answer the following question.

How effectively does the writer explore the view expressed in the opening sentence of the extract that "death has changed for modern man"?

You should support your answer with detailed reference to:

- structure
- tone
- language and imagery.

They say death has changed for modern man, that it has been deconstructed and, like him, become postmodern. Sometimes when the day is bright and blue and hot enough to be quite empty, and the rocks shimmer in the sun, the conviction comes that at their heart human societies are just elaborate fabrications for suppressing a 5 knowledge of death—conspiracies sufficiently complex and beguiling that the dark secret of our own mortality no longer obtrudes. This huge artifice protects the race against its Achilles heel—the certainty that all its affairs are nothing.

On the morning wind we seem to hear the creak of a million treadmills, the squeak of rowing machines, the trilling and drilling of an endless aerobics class. It is the dawn 10 chorus of anxiety. A kind of insurance is being enacted, that private/public investment in keeping fit and being seen to be keeping fit. Apart from exacting its own toll in humourless tedium, it turns ill health into a personal failure, so that death is seen as just deserts for not having taken the trouble to be sufficiently alive. The body as machine, the unread user's manual, the culpable lack of maintenance: they all form a 15 nexus of irresponsibility and downfall. Someone fails to turn up at the gym as usual in their Lycra leotard. After a few days their name escapes us. It is understood there was always something more they might have done: another few yards' jogging a day, many fewer beers and cigarettes, a further notch of health reached in order to carry on being fit indefinitely. (What was it we failed to grasp even as we hung punitively from wall 20 bars? Does the mind rot atop its splendid torso?)

In what pathetic fragments we move, believing ourselves whole! The precious "I" disappears for long stretches each day and entirely vanishes during sleep. In one of our registers something never forgets a refrigerator door is always yawning for us as the prelude to spade or flames. Here, at least, the old mythologies no longer work as they 25 did. It is not possible to envisage a private survival. There can be no magic left in prophecies of paradise. That all life was held to have begun in a garden and—if we are good—will likewise end in one convinces hardly anyone. Soon, two-thirds of the world's people will be town-dwellers, to whom rural metaphors are no longer instinctive. Since most people who imagine life after death think of their ordinary life 30 transfigured, a townie would find the myth of the celestial city more plausible than that of a garden paradise.

There is pathos in the way religions of the book have become immovably beached on the littorals of far away and long ago. To desert-dwellers, what more natural than to see heaven as a sublime oasis which owes its existence to nothing more mystical than 35 *water*? Here we are, the deserving, eternally at peace in a lush garden, sprawled in the

shade and recovering after life's gruelling journey. The essence of paradise will always be conflated with that of lost Eden, since the future is unimaginable and the present unmythic. The very word "paradise" comes from Persian via Greek and means a park. What could the modern world offer by way of a matching tranquil and timeless vision?
40 Are we to recline for ever in some leafy municipal square, where the sun filtering through the trees dapples us in a bearable radiance, where traffic noise has ceased, where litter-free paths are strolled by the righteous eating ambrosial hamburgers? It doesn't work. Nor does a Southern Californian dream of bronzing our cancer-proof skin beside Hockney-blue pools, endlessly dating and mating and clinching deals.
45 Besides lacking depth, such visions have no ecstasy. In any case, our bodily needs are now largely catered for. It is impossible to imagine any central image as simple and important as *water* which might resonate for us as a condition of life itself. And this is the triumph of material mastery: that it supersedes and blots out the symbolic to the extent that the only resounding things left are absences. Nature has fallen beneath
50 *Homo*'s power, and in doing so has left him without an image of heaven.

In distant archipelagos there are often days of heat and dazzle powerful enough to wipe out thought, to leach away everything that is not planetary furniture: trees, rocks, clouds and water, to the horizon. To people who skitter about these gulfs of ocean in pea-pod craft—a few sheets of marine plywood tacked together with copper
55 nails—death is an imminent presence. So it is for those hacking at their stony fields high above the glittering shoreline. Subsistence throws things into bright relief. At the end of the day's work either there are fish and maize cobs to be laid over charcoal or there are not. Infants are born, linger for a week, vanish into the ground. There are no hidden deals. Everything—shelter, food, water—is plain. The facts are dealt with by
60 private treaty. The woman pounding her washing on a stone in the stream, the plodder behind his buffalo knee-deep in a rice paddy, the lone fisherman far out in the sun's glare: each might harbour wistful dreams, but none pretends to be proof against the cancellation which can descend in an instant, whimsically, without notice or reprieve. The beaches on which their children romp and tumble are composed of the dead. The
65 whole landscape is a cemetery. Diatom, mollusc, foraminifer, cuttlebone, dog jaw, pig tooth, and all by the trillion ton. Daily they walk on the deepening past, mend nets on it, fall asleep on it, make cement blocks with it, shit into it. The sea turns over and over, a geological machine smoothly meshing its gears and grinding up time itself. At night it sparkles with energy. Sit beside it under the stars, and fan the driftwood
70 embers and watch very seriously the broiling fish as slowly they curve upwards from the heat. Not as dead as they look, some of them, for now and then one leaps off the coals the instant it is laid across them. "*Buhay pa!*" and a child's delighted scurry to retrieve it and place it on the fire again. "Lie down! Go to sleep!" Companionable laughter. The incense of smouldering fish oil drifts across the constellations and
75 brings the village dogs from far down the beach.

Despite the skinniness of this living, for all its rigour, there can exist in these rural and marine backwaters a certain ebullience. Not to sentimentalize it, it is that peculiar freedom which descends like a gift on those so constantly menaced that they slip off the burden of mere worry. A strange security results when death is so close a
80 companion. It can be felt while crunching along a beach, a skeleton walking on skeletons with the time machine turning in step, wavefalls and footfalls. A gleeful levity at being so brief, at feeling so exempt. Freedom from what, then? Certainly not from the irreducible pact of living. Rather, from the heaviness of having to share in metropolitan anxieties, the contaminating conspiracy, the yearning. Freedom, too,
85 from the corroding suspicion that the extra time bought by wall bars has already gone on wall bars.

3. Poetry [*Page thirty-two*]

Read carefully the poem **Seen from the Train** *(1948) by C. Day Lewis and then answer the questions that follow it.*

SEEN FROM THE TRAIN

Somewhere between Crewkerne
And Yeovil it was. On the left of the line
Just as the crinkled hills unroll
To the plain. A church on a small green knoll—
5 A limestone church,
And above the church
Cedar boughs stretched like hands that yearn
To protect or to bless. The whole

Stood up, antique and clear
10 As a cameo, from the vale. I swear
It was not a dream. Twice, thrice had I found it
Chancing to look as my train wheeled round it.
But this time I passed,
Though I gazed as I passed
15 All the way down the valley, that knoll was not there,
Nor the church, nor the trees it mounded.

What came between to unsight me? . . .
But suppose, only suppose there might be
A secret look in a landscape's eye
20 Following you as you hasten by,
And you have your chance—
Two or three chances
At most—to hold and interpret it rightly,
Or it is gone for aye.

25 There was a time when men
Would have called it a vision, said that sin
Had blinded me since to a heavenly fact.
Well, I have neither invoked nor faked
Any church in the air,
30 And little I care
Whether or no I shall see it again.
But blindly my heart is racked

When I think how, not twice or thrice,
But year after year in another's eyes
35 I have caught the look that I missed today
Of the church, the knoll, the cedars—a ray
Of the faith, too, they stood for,
The hope they were food for,
The love they prayed for, facts beyond price—
40 And turned my eyes away.

Drawing evidence from the poet's use of word choice and imagery, structure and rhyme, and any other technical aspects of the poem that you think are significant, answer the following questions.

(*a*) What is the nature of the experience presented by the poet in lines 1–16 and how effectively does he describe it?

(*b*) How does the poet react, in lines 17–31, to the experience he has described in the first two stanzas?

(*c*) Why do you think he says, in line 32, "But blindly my heart is racked"?

4. Drama [*Pages thirty-three to thirty-nine*]

The following extract is from Act One, Scene 2 of ***The Winslow Boy*** (1946) *by Terence Rattigan. The play is set in the period just before the First World War and deals with the events that follow the expulsion of Ronnie Winslow from Osborne Royal Naval College for the alleged theft of a postal order from a fellow cadet. His father, Arthur Winslow, is convinced of Ronnie's innocence and feels that his son has been unjustly treated because he has had no opportunity to defend himself. After a year of fruitless campaigning, Arthur's last hope is to persuade the great advocate, Sir Robert Morton, to take the case and establish Ronnie's innocence in court. In this scene, which forms the climax to the first act, Sir Robert is deciding whether or not he will accept the case.*

Characters in the scene:

RONNIE WINSLOW
ARTHUR WINSLOW — his father
GRACE WINSLOW — his mother
CATHERINE WINSLOW — his sister
DICKIE WINSLOW — his elder brother
DESMOND CURRY — solicitor
JOHN WATHERSTONE — Catherine's fiancé
SIR ROBERT MORTON K.C.

Read the extract carefully and then answer the following question.

Make a close, critical study of the extract in which you analyse and evaluate the means by which

- dramatic tension is created
- audience sympathies are manipulated.

(RONNIE *comes in, looking very spick and span.*)

ARTHUR: This is my son, Ronald. Ronnie, this is Sir Robert Morton.

RONNIE: How do you do, sir? (*He shakes hands with* SIR ROBERT.)

ARTHUR: He is going to ask you a few questions. You must answer them all
5 truthfully—as you always have. (*He begins to struggle out of his chair.*) I expect you would like us to leave—

SIR ROBERT: No, provided, of course, that you don't interrupt. (*To* CATHERINE) Miss Winslow, will you sit down, please?

(CATHERINE *sits.*)

10 (*To* RONNIE) Will you stand at the table, facing me?

(RONNIE *does so.*)

That's right.

(*He faces* RONNIE *across the table and begins his examination very quietly.*) How old are you?

15 RONNIE: Fourteen and seven months.

SIR ROBERT: You were, then, thirteen and ten months old when you left Osborne; is that right?

RONNIE: Yes, sir.

SIR ROBERT: Now I would like you to cast your mind back to July 7th of last year.
20 Will you tell me in your own words exactly what happened to you on that day?

RONNIE: All right. Well, it was a half-holiday, so we didn't have any work after dinner—

SIR ROBERT: Dinner?

25 RONNIE: Yes. At one o'clock. Until prep. at seven—

SIR ROBERT: Prep. at seven?

RONNIE: Yes. Just before dinner I went to the Chief Petty Officer and asked him to let me have fifteen and six out of what I had in the College Bank—

30 SIR ROBERT: Why did you do that?

RONNIE: I wanted to buy an air-pistol.

SIR ROBERT: Which cost fifteen and six?

RONNIE: Yes, sir.

SIR ROBERT: And how much money did you have in the College bank at the time?

35 RONNIE: Two pounds three shillings.

ARTHUR: So you see, sir, what incentive could there possibly be for him to steal five shillings?

SIR ROBERT: (*coldly*): I must ask you to be good enough not to interrupt me, sir. (*To* RONNIE) After you had withdrawn the fifteen and six, what did
40 you do?

RONNIE: I had dinner.

SIR ROBERT: Then what?

RONNIE: I went to the locker-room and put the fifteen and six in my locker.

SIR ROBERT: Yes. Then?

45 RONNIE: I went to get permission to go down to the post office. Then I went to the locker-room again, got out my money, and went down to the post office.

SIR ROBERT: I see. Go on.

RONNIE: I bought my postal order—

50 SIR ROBERT: For fifteen and six?

RONNIE: Yes. Then I went back to college. Then I met Elliot minor, and he said: "I say, isn't it rot? Someone's broken into my locker and pinched a postal order. I've reported it to the P.O."

SIR ROBERT: Those were Elliot minor's exact words?

55 RONNIE: He might have used another word for rot—

SIR ROBERT: I see. Continue—

RONNIE: Well then, just before prep., I was told to go along and see Commander Flower. The woman from the post office was there, and the Commander said: "Is this the boy?" and she said, "It might be. I can't be sure. They all look so much alike." 60

ARTHUR: You see? She couldn't identify him.

(SIR ROBERT *glares at* ARTHUR.)

SIR ROBERT: (*to* RONNIE): Go on.

RONNIE: Then she said: "I only know that the boy who bought a postal order for fifteen and six was the same boy that cashed one for five shillings." 65 So the Commander said: "Did you buy a postal order for fifteen and six?" And I said, "Yes," and then they made me write Elliot minor's name on an envelope, and compared it to the signature on the postal order—then they sent me to the sanatorium, and ten days later I was sacked—I mean—expelled. 70

SIR ROBERT: I see. (*He rises. Quietly*): Did you cash a postal order belonging to Elliot minor for five shillings?

RONNIE: No, sir.

SIR ROBERT: Did you break into his locker and steal it?

75 RONNIE: No, sir.

(DICKIE *enters. He stands furtively in the doorway, not knowing whether to come in or go out.*)

SIR ROBERT: And that is the truth, the whole truth, and nothing but the truth?

RONNIE: Yes, sir.

80 (ARTHUR *waves* DICKIE *impatiently to come and stand behind his chair.*)

SIR ROBERT: Right. When the Commander asked you to write Elliot's name on an envelope, how did you write it? With Christian name or initials?

RONNIE: I wrote: "Charles K. Elliot."

SIR ROBERT: Charles K. Elliot. Did you by any chance happen to see the forged postal order in the Commander's office? 85

RONNIE: Oh yes. The Commander showed it to me.

SIR ROBERT: Before or after you had written Elliot's name on the envelope?

RONNIE: After.

SIR ROBERT: After. And did you happen to see how Elliot's name was written on the postal order? 90

RONNIE: Yes, sir. The same.

SIR ROBERT: The same? Charles K. Elliot.

RONNIE: Yes, sir.

SIR ROBERT: When you wrote on the envelope—what made you choose that particular form? 95

RONNIE: That was the way he usually signed his name.

SIR ROBERT: How did you know?

RONNIE: Well—he was a friend of mine—

	SIR ROBERT:	That is no answer. How did you know?
100	RONNIE:	I'd seen him sign things.
	SIR ROBERT:	What things?
	RONNIE:	Oh—ordinary things.
	SIR ROBERT:	I repeat—what things?
	RONNIE:	(*reluctantly*): Bits of paper.
105	SIR ROBERT:	Bits of paper? And why did he sign his name on bits of paper?
	RONNIE:	I don't know.
	SIR ROBERT:	You do know. Why did he sign his name on bits of paper?
	RONNIE:	He was practising his signature.
	SIR ROBERT:	And you saw him?
110	RONNIE:	Yes.
	SIR ROBERT:	Did he know you saw him?
	RONNIE:	Well—yes—
	SIR ROBERT:	In other words, he showed you exactly how he wrote his signature?
	RONNIE:	Yes. I suppose he did.
115	SIR ROBERT:	Did you practise writing it yourself?
	RONNIE:	I might have done.
	SIR ROBERT:	What do you mean, you might have done? Did you, or did you not?
	RONNIE:	Yes.
	ARTHUR:	(*sharply*): Ronnie! You never told me that.
120	RONNIE:	It was only for a joke—
	SIR ROBERT:	Never mind whether it was for a joke or not. The fact is, you practised forging Elliot's signature.
	RONNIE:	It wasn't forging—
	SIR ROBERT:	What do you call it then?
125	RONNIE:	Writing.
	SIR ROBERT:	Very well. Writing. Whoever stole the postal order and cashed it also *wrote* Elliot's signature, didn't he?
	RONNIE:	Yes.
130	SIR ROBERT:	And, oddly enough, in the exact form in which you had earlier been practising *writing* his signature.
	RONNIE:	(*indignantly*): I say! Which side are you on?
	SIR ROBERT:	(*snarling*): Don't be impertinent! (*He consults a document.*) Are you aware that the Admiralty sent up the forged postal order to Mr. Ridgley-Pearce—the greatest handwriting expert in England?
135	RONNIE:	Yes.
	SIR ROBERT:	And you know that Mr. Ridgley-Pearce affirmed that there was no doubt that the signature on the postal order and the signature you wrote on the envelope were by one and the same hand?
	RONNIE:	Yes.

140 SIR ROBERT: And you still say that you didn't forge that signature?

RONNIE: Yes, I do.

SIR ROBERT: In other words, Mr. Ridgley-Pearce doesn't know his job?

RONNIE: Well, he's wrong, anyway.

SIR ROBERT: When you went into the locker room after lunch, were you alone?

145 RONNIE: I don't remember.

SIR ROBERT: I think you do. Were you alone in the locker room?

RONNIE: Yes.

SIR ROBERT: And you knew which was Elliot's locker?

RONNIE: Yes, of course.

150 SIR ROBERT: Why did you go in there at all?

RONNIE: I've told you. To put my fifteen and six away.

SIR ROBERT: Why?

RONNIE: I thought it would be safer.

SIR ROBERT: Why safer than your pocket?

155 RONNIE: I don't know.

SIR ROBERT: You had it in your pocket at dinner-time. Why this sudden fear for its safety?

RONNIE: (*plainly rattled*): I tell you I don't know—

SIR ROBERT: It was rather an odd thing to do, wasn't it? The money was perfectly
160 safe in your pocket. Why did you suddenly feel yourself impelled to put it away in your locker?

RONNIE: (*almost shouting*): I don't know.

SIR ROBERT: Was it because you knew you would be alone in the locker room at that time?

165 RONNIE: No.

SIR ROBERT: Where was Elliot's locker in relation to yours?

RONNIE: Next to it, but one.

SIR ROBERT: Next but one. What time did Elliot put his postal order in his locker?

RONNIE: I don't know. I didn't even know he had a postal order in his locker.
170 I didn't know he had a postal order at all.

SIR ROBERT: Yet you say he was a great friend of yours—

RONNIE: He didn't tell me he had one.

SIR ROBERT: How very secretive of him. (*He makes a note on the document.*) What time did you go to the locker room?

175 RONNIE: I don't remember.

SIR ROBERT: Was it directly after dinner?

RONNIE: Yes, I think so.

SIR ROBERT: What did you do after leaving the locker room?

RONNIE: I've told you. I went for permission to go to the post office.

180 SIR ROBERT: What time was that?

RONNIE: About a quarter past two.

SIR ROBERT: Dinner is over at a quarter to two. Which means that you were alone in the locker room for half an hour?

RONNIE: I wasn't there all that time—

185 SIR ROBERT: How long were you there?

RONNIE: About five minutes.

SIR ROBERT: What were you doing for the other twenty-five?

RONNIE: I don't remember.

SIR ROBERT: It's odd that your memory is so good about some things and so bad
190 about others—

RONNIE: Perhaps I waited outside the C.O.'s office.

SIR ROBERT: (*with searing sarcasm*): Perhaps you waited outside the C.O.'s office. And perhaps no one saw you there, either?

RONNIE: No. I don't think they did.

195 SIR ROBERT: What were you thinking about outside the C.O.'s office for twenty-five minutes?

RONNIE: (*wildly*): I don't even know if I was there. I can't remember. Perhaps I wasn't there at all.

SIR ROBERT: No. Perhaps you were still in the locker room rifling Elliot's locker—

200 ARTHUR: (*indignantly*): Sir Robert, I must ask you—

SIR ROBERT: Quiet!

RONNIE: I remember now. I remember. Someone did see me outside the C.O.'s office. A chap called Casey. I remember I spoke to him.

SIR ROBERT: What did you say?

205 RONNIE: I said: "Come down to the post office with me. I'm going to cash a postal order."

SIR ROBERT: (*triumphantly*): *Cash* a postal order.

RONNIE: I mean get.

SIR ROBERT: You said cash. Why did you say cash if you meant get?

210 RONNIE: I don't know.

SIR ROBERT: I suggest cash was the truth.

RONNIE: No, no. It wasn't. It wasn't really. You're muddling me.

SIR ROBERT: You seem easily muddled. How many other lies have you told?

RONNIE: None. Really I haven't.

215 SIR ROBERT: (*bending forward malevolently*): I suggest your whole testimony is a lie.

RONNIE: No! It's the truth.

SIR ROBERT: I suggest there is barely one single word of truth in anything you have said either to me, or to the Judge Advocate or to the Commander. I
220 suggest that you broke into Elliot's locker, that you stole the postal order for five shillings belonging to Elliot, and you cashed it by means of forging his name.

RONNIE: (*wailing*): I didn't. I didn't.

SIR ROBERT: I suggest you did it for a joke, meaning to give Elliot the five shillings
225 back, but that when you met him and he said he had reported the matter that you got frightened and decided to keep quiet.

RONNIE: No, no, no. It isn't true.

SIR ROBERT: I suggest that by continuing to deny your guilt you are causing great hardship to your own family, and considerable annoyance to high and
230 important persons in this country—

CATHERINE: (*on her feet*): That's a disgraceful thing to say!

ARTHUR: (*rising*): I agree.

SIR ROBERT: (*leaning forward and glaring at* RONNIE *with utmost venom*): I suggest that the time has at last come for you to undo some of the misery you
235 have caused by confessing to us all now that you are a forger, a liar and a thief.

(GRACE *rises, crosses swiftly to* RONNIE *and envelops him.*)

RONNIE: (*in tears*): I'm not! I'm not! I'm not! I didn't do it.

ARTHUR: This is outrageous, sir.

240 (DESMOND *crosses above* SIR ROBERT *to the table and collects the documents.* JOHN *enters. He is dressed in evening clothes.*)

JOHN: Kate, dear, I'm late. I'm terribly sorry—

(*He stops short as he takes in the scene.* RONNIE *is sobbing hysterically on his mother's breast.* ARTHUR *and* CATHERINE *are glaring indignantly at*
245 SIR ROBERT*, who is putting his papers together.*)

SIR ROBERT: (*to* DESMOND): Can I drop you anywhere? My car is at the door.

DESMOND: Er—no—I thank you.

SIR ROBERT: (*carelessly*): Well, send all this stuff round to my chambers to-morrow morning, will you?

250 DESMOND: But—but will you need it now?

SIR ROBERT: Oh, yes. The boy is plainly innocent. I accept the brief.

(SIR ROBERT *bows to* ARTHUR *and* CATHERINE *and walks languidly to the door past the bewildered* JOHN*, to whom he gives a polite nod as he goes out.* RONNIE *continues to sob hysterically.*)

QUICK CURTAIN

[Turn over

Section 4—Reading the Media

You must answer **one question only** in this section.

Category A—Film

1. "*It's tremendously satisfying to use the cinematic art to achieve mass emotion, to arouse by pure film, not by subject matter or performance.*"

   (Alfred Hitchcock)

   Bearing in mind what Hitchcock has said, show how any **one** director has used "*the cinematic art*" (i.e. the language of film) as the primary means of engaging the emotions of the audience.

   In your answer, you should make close reference to sequences from **one** or **more than one** film.

2. Make a detailed analysis of any **one** film in order to demonstrate that it not only works within established generic conventions but also reworks these conventions to reflect issues of its time.

Category B—Television

3. "*Personalities are central to the success of certain types of programme: they act as an assurance that audiences will return again and again.*"

   Discuss with reference to any **two** of the following: news, sport, current affairs, lifestyle, documentary programmes.

4. "*Television soap opera has the great advantage of time—time for the development of character and complex story lines.*"

   How effectively does any **one** television soap opera make use of such time?

Category C—Radio

5. "*Drama thrives on radio by stretching the listener's imagination.*"

   Discuss.

6. "*Although local radio stations do carry local elements like news, sport and phone-ins, they are dominated by cosmopolitan pop music culture.*"

   To what extent do you consider this to be a fair description of the output of any **one** local radio station?

Category D—Print journalism

7. In this question you are presented with extracts from *The Independent*'s coverage of the ceremony held in London on 4 August 2004 to mark the 90th anniversary of the start of the Great War.

On *Page forty-two*, you are provided with a copy of the front page of the newspaper and, on *Page forty-three*, materials from elsewhere in the newspaper.

Analyse the images and texts employed and evaluate their effectiveness in conveying the significance of the occasion.

[Turn over

Newspaper of the Year

THE INDEPENDENT

No 5,554 www.independent.co.uk THURSDAY 5 AUGUST 2004 (Republic of Ireland €0.95) 60p

The power and glory of Henri Cartier-Bresson
TRIBUTE TO A GREAT PHOTOGRAPHER, PAGES 24 & 25

Summer fashion
Sleek swimsuits & cool capes plus Dylan Jones
REVIEW, PAGES 12 - 15

On 4 August 1914, the Great War began. 900,000 Britons perished. Ninety years on, just four veterans were able to honour the fallen.

The last survivors

Henry Allingham, at 108 Britain's oldest war veteran, laid the wreath at the Cenotaph yesterday to commemorate his fallen comrades *David Sandison*

BY CAHAL MILMO

NINETY YEARS ago, an 18 year-old apprentice mechanic called Henry Allingham rushed to a crowded London recruiting office to sign up to fight against Germany.

He was one of nine million men and women from Britain and its dominions who would head for the battlefields of the First World War. By its end, more than 8·5 million soldiers of all nations lay dead. Some 900,000 of them were British.

A quarter of the male British population went to fight; five million of them were either killed or wounded. At 11am yesterday – nine decades since the summer's day of 4 August 1914 that marked the outbreak of the Great War – Mr Allingham sat alongside three of his former comrades in front of the Cenotaph in Whitehall to honour those they had left behind.

It was probably the last time that Britain's soldiers of the Great War would see such an event – an event in which a crowd of 1,000 people broke into spontaneous applause and some openly wept.

For Mr Allingham, Britain oldest veteran at 108, it was the day to both remember and forget. He said: "When it started I didn't know what to expect. I thought we'd win, I thought we wouldn't have to fight again like that for 100 years.

"I will never forget my comrades. You cannot think about the morbid things that took place. If you did, you could not go on. But on days like this I pray for them."

Frail of sight and step, the four men were the only ones among the 23 surviving veterans of the Great War who were still able to come to the Cenotaph. Ultimately, they explained, they were soldiers who had fought for their families and for each other, only to pay a price they can never forget.

Fred Lloyd, 106, who had joined up to be with his two brothers, Bill and Tom, said: "War is not something nice to remember. There is nothing wonderful about it. I wanted to help Bill and Tom. But I couldn't in the end."

Centurions guarding memory of millions, pages 14 &15

The centurions guarding the memory of millions that fell

Four of the handful of surviving combatants from the First World War met at the Cenotaph yesterday to mark the 90th anniversary of the conflict's outbreak. **Cahal Milmo** tells their remarkable stories.

The four veterans at the Cenotaph ceremony yesterday. From left to right Bill Stone, Henry Allingham, Fred Lloyd and John Oborne. *David Sandison*

'I fell into one of the holes. It was full of bodies and blood.'

THE FOURTH of August 1914—when Britain declared war on Germany and some 11 million men started the march to Europe's bloodiest war—was spent by Henry Allingham doing what he loved best: trying to ride a motorbike.

Then 18, he travelled to London's Piccadilly to queue at the recruiting office of the Royal Engineers to try to enlist as a despatch rider because he wanted to exchange his Triumph motorbike for the more powerful military machines.

Unfortunately, some 200 others had had a similar idea and got to Piccadilly ahead of him. He was rejected, and Mr Allingham joined a fledgling arm of British military aviation, the Royal Naval Air Service (RNAS). Rather than riding a bike, he witnessed the extremes of the First World War on land and sea, from the Battle of Jutland to the third Battle of Ypres in which the British alone suffered 400,000 casualties.

Now 108, Mr Allingham is Britain's oldest surviving war veteran. But yesterday, nine decades had done little to dim his memory of what he saw, or his desire to tell others of the grotesque nature of conflict.

As he sat alongside three of the remaining 23 known survivors of the Great War in front of the Cenotaph, he explained his almost evangelical desire to talk about his military career.

He said: "It is my duty to talk about my experiences and the horror of war. Most who have been to war never want to do it again. There was good comradeship but it was no fun."

The veteran, who still lives in his third-floor flat in Eastbourne and has his meals delivered to him by carers, had his first taste of battle on HMS *Kingfisher* in 1916 when he was in an airborne spotter force sent to find the German fleet.

He witnessed Jutland, the battle of a Danish peninsula that confined the German navy to port for the war, and remembers the sound of heavy enemy shells passing over his destroyer. He realised the importance of the battle only at a church service after the battle, when the vicar offered a prayer for the "victory of Jutland".

After the war, Mr Allingham married his fiancée, Dorothy, and they had two daughters. Such is his great age that he has outlived all of them. But his most vivid memories are of the Western Front, where he often had to take his chances in the highly dangerous no man's land to help recover damaged aircraft. Often, he had to shelter from artillery barrages in vast shell-holes infested with rats and filled with the dismembered remains of many of his comrades.

He said: "Once, during Ypres, I fell into one of the holes. It was dark and I struggled. I thought I would drown but I managed to get a footing. I dragged myself out. It was full of bodies and blood. That is something you don't forget."

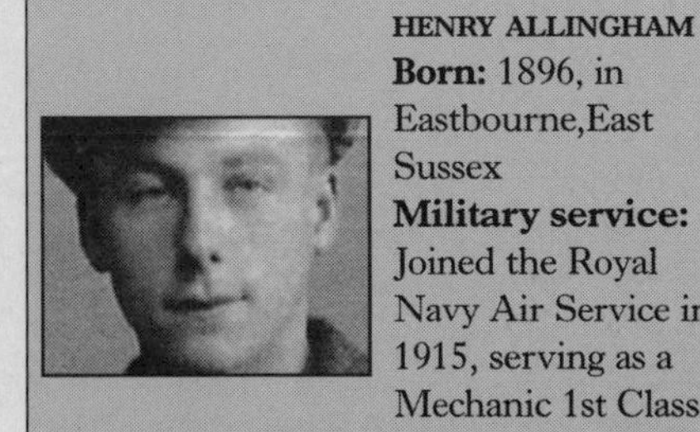

HENRY ALLINGHAM
Born: 1896, in Eastbourne, East Sussex
Military service: Joined the Royal Navy Air Service in 1915, serving as a Mechanic 1st Class. Fought at Jutland and Passchendaele.
Post-war: Returned to pre-war job as a car mechanic and married his fiancée, Dorothy. They had two daughters. During the Second World War he was an aircraft mechanic.

8. Drawing evidence from a **range** of materials (including, if you wish, the materials provided for **Question 7**), how far do you agree that "*newspaper stories turn real life into fiction and real people into stereotypes, leading readers to make simplistic judgements and evaluations*"?

Category E—Advertising

9. For this question you are provided (as separate colour inserts) with two advertisements, both from *In Style* magazine, August 2004.

Discuss the means by which these advertisements seek to extend brand loyalty by investing new versions of existing products with distinctive identities.

10. "*However forward looking advertising may pretend to be, it is essentially traditional in its assumptions, relying on well-worn representations of age, class, gender, race, nation.*"

How far do you agree?

In answering this question, you must refer to a **range** of individual advertisements (including, if you wish, the advertisements provided for **Question 9**).

[*END OF QUESTION PAPER*]

THE
FORGIVEN
A Delicate Version
Mars Delight
of a Classic

IT'S JUST THE THING FOR US SENSITIVE TYPES
Quintin is an expert when it comes to sensitive skin and that's why he recommends Comfort Pure to everyone who visits his beauty spa. He knows that because it's hypoallergenic, it's the perfect treatment for sensitive customers of all ages.
Comfort Pure Made purely for sensitive skin
Hypoallergenic
Comfort
Pure

[BLANK PAGE]

[BLANK PAGE]

[BLANK PAGE]

[BLANK PAGE]

[BLANK PAGE]

[BLANK PAGE]

[BLANK PAGE]

Acknowledgements

Leckie & Leckie is grateful to the copyright holders, as credited, for permission to use their material:
Extract from *The Anatomist* by James Bridie. Reproduced by permission of The Agency (London) Ltd © The Estate of James Bridie. First published by Constable and Co Ltd. All rights reserved and enquiries to The Agency (London) Ltd 24 Pottery Lane, London W11 4LZ info@theagency.co.uk (2003 p 2–4);
Extract from *Lanark* by Alasdair Gray, first published in 1981 by Canongate Books, 14 High Street, Edinburgh, EH1 1TE (2003 pp 21–22);
The Sun for the articles 'Brit lit's a hit' © NI Syndication, London 2002 (2004 p 19) and 'Why Hollywood babes are queuing up to play literary giants in cardies' by Katy Weitz © NI Syndication, London 2002 (2004 p 20);
Luath Press Ltd for the poem 'Wi a Naukit Dirkie' by William Neill taken from *Caledonian Cramboclink* (2004 p 23);
The article 'A Stiletto in the Tories' Hearts' by George Jones & Andrews Sparrow taken from *The Daily Telegraph* © Telegraph Group Limited 2002 (2004 p 41);
'Crush' is taken from *Mean Time* by Carol Ann Duffy, published by Anvil Press Poetry in 1993 (2005 p 4);
Article from *The Sun* February 9, 2004 © NI Syndication, London (2005 p 17);
David Nicol for an extract from *The Fundamentals of New Caledonia* (2005 p 21–23);
Nick Hern Books for an extract from the play *Iron* by Rona Munro (2005 p 36–43);
The article 'Becks: I am Livid' from *The Sun* February 18, 2003 © NI Syndication, London (2005 p 46);
Carcanet Press for the poem 'To Joan Eardley' by Edwin Morgan, taken from *Poems of Thirty Years* (2006 p 6);
Canongate Educational for an extract from Highland River by Neil M Gunn (2006 p 9);
The article 'Scottish Sun is the Toast of Holyrood' by Kenny McAlpine, taken from *The Sun,* September 3, 2004 © NI Syndication, London (2006 p 19);
Johnson & Alcock Literary Agency for an extract from 'Sea Burial' by James Hamilton-Paterson, taken from *Granta 61* (2006 p 31);
The poem 'Seen from the Train' from *The Complete Poems* by C. Day Lewis, published by Sinclair-Stevenson (1992). Copyright © 1992 in this edition The Estate of C Day Lewis. Reprinted by permission of The Random House Group Ltd (2006 p 32);

The following companies/individuals have very generously given permission to reproduce their copyright material free of charge:
Scottish Parliamentary copyright material is reproduced with the permission of the Queen's Printer for Scotland on behalf of the Scottish Parliamentary Corporate body (2003 p 5–7);
Extract from 'Willie Rough' by Bill Bryden, in *Scots Plays of the Seventies: An Anthology*, edited by Bill Findlay and published by Scottish Cultural Press, ISBN: 1 84017 028 X, £12.99. (2003 pp 11–13);
Extract from 'A Piece of Chalk' by GK Chesterton, from *A Book of English Essays* edited by WE Williams. Reprinted by permission of AP Watt Ltd on behalf of The Royal Literary Fund. (2003 pp 28–30);
Random House for the poem 'Unwittingly' by John Burnside, taken from *A Normal Skin* (2003 p 31);
Extract from 'Roots' by Arnold Wesker, taken from *The Wesker Trilogy*, published by Penguin. Reproduced by permission of Sir Arnold Wesker. 'Roots' is the second play in a trilogy of plays known as THE WESKER TRILOGY which has, over the years, sold around 400,000 copies. The volume is available published by Methuen Books, priced £12.99. Probably cheaper via Amazon. (2003 pp 32–37);
Art & Commerce for an advertisement (2003 p 40);
L.G. Harris & Co. for an advertisement (2003 p 41);
'Doing collegiality and keeping control at work: small talk in government departments' by Janet Holmes, taken from *Small Talk* edited by Justine Coupland. Published by Pearson Education Ltd. (2004 pp 15–16);
Jim Wallace for an extract from a speech (2004 pp 16–18);
The Scots Language Resource Centre for an extract from *Scotspeak* by Christine Robertson & Carol Ann Crawford (2004 pp 21–22);
Greentrax Recordings for the lyrics to 'Oor Hamlet' by Adam McNaughton (2004 p 23);
An extract from *Gentlemen in England* by A.N. Wilson. Reprinted by permission of Peters Fraser & Dunlop Group on behalf of A.N. Wilson © A.N. Wilson 1985 (2004 pp 24–25);
An extract from *The Story of Lucy Gault* by William Trevor (Penguin Books, 2002) © William Trevor, 2002 (2004 pp 25–26);
Granta for an extract from *Among Chickens* by Jonathan Miller (2004 pp 27–30);
Extract from *No Hiding Place* by Tracy Herd, (Bloodaxe Books, 1996) (2004 p 31);
ICI plc for an advertisement. 'Dulux', 'Once' and the Old English Sheepdog are trademarks of ICI. (2004 p 43);
The Provost and Scholars of King's College, Cambridge and the Society of Authors as the Literary Representatives of the EM Forster Estate. Extract from *Howards End* by EM Forster (2005 p 8);
SAGE Publications Ltd for an extract from 'Conversation Analysis: An approach to the study of social action as sense-making practices' by Anita Pomerantz & BJ Fehr, taken from *Discourse as Social Interaction* edited by Teun wan Dijk (2005 pp 13–14);
David McLetchie for an extract from a speech (2005 pp 15–16);
SCOTS Project for an extract from 'SCOTS Project, Conversation 06' by Dr John Corbett (2005 pp 18–20);
Neal Ascherson for an article from *The Herald Magazine*, 28th August 2004 (2005 pp 28–32);
Seren Books for an extract from the poem *Jugged Hare* by Jean Earle, taken from *Selected Poems* (2005 p 34);
The Independent for an article from Tuesday 18th February 2003 (2005 p 47);
Her Majesty's Stationary Office for an extract from *Official Report of the Scottish Parliament,* 8th September 2004 (2006 pp 16–18);
SCOTS Project for an extract from 'Conversation 05: Fife couple on shared memories' Document 348, by Dr Anderson, taken from *SCOTS Project* (2006 pp 20–22);
Janet Paisley for the poem 'Sharleen: Ah'm Shy', taken from *The Kist* (2006 p 23);
Birlinn Ltd for the poem 'Almost Miss Scotland' by Liz Lochhead, taken from *The Colour of Black and White* (2006 p 24);
Extract from *Brick Lane* by Monica Ali, published by Doubleday, 2003. Reprinted by permission of The Random House Group Ltd (2006 pp 25–29);
Pearson Education for an extract from 'The Winslow Boy' (1946) by T Rattigan, taken from *Heritage of Literature Series* (2006 pp 33-39);
An advertisement for Comfort Pure, reproduced with kind permission of Unilever (2006 p 46).